Young Writers 2005

PLAYGRO

Let your creativity flow...

- The Adventure Starts Here
Edited by Jessica Woodbridge

 Young**Writers**

First published in Great Britain in 2005 by:
Young Writers
Remus House
Coltsfoot Drive
Peterborough
PE2 9JX
Telephone: 01733 890066
Website: www.youngwriters.co.uk

SB ISBN 1 84602 307 6

Foreword

Young Writers was established in 1991 and has been passionately devoted to the promotion of reading and writing in children and young adults ever since. The quest continues today. Young Writers remains as committed to the fostering of burgeoning poetic and literary talent as ever.

This year's Young Writers competition has proven as vibrant and dynamic as ever and we are delighted to present a showcase of the best poetry from across the UK. Each poem has been carefully selected from a wealth of *Playground Poets* entries before ultimately being published in this, our thirteenth primary school poetry series.

Once again, we have been supremely impressed by the overall high quality of the entries we have received. The imagination, energy and creativity which has gone into each young writer's entry made choosing the best poems a challenging and often difficult but ultimately hugely rewarding task - the general high standard of the work submitted amply vindicating this opportunity to bring their poetry to a larger appreciative audience.

We sincerely hope you are pleased with our final selection and that you will enjoy *Playground Poets - The Adventure Starts Here* for many years to come.

Contents

Chloe Kirk (11)   18
Andrew Oglesby (11)   18
Lucy Smith (11)   19
Adam Billyard (11)   19
Tom Bannister (12)   19
Adam Nicholls (11)   20
Christian Lyth (11)   20
Lauren-Mae Pearson (11)   21
Kathryn Cook (11)   21
Harry Price (11)   22
Shahin Jogi (11)   22
Sophie Rasen (11)   23
Claudia Taws (11)   23
Katie Stalker (11)   24
Tom Wiles (10)   24
Caycee Peskett-Hill (10)   25
Sean Riglin (11)   25
Nathan Williamson (11)   26
Elsie Machell (11)   26
Katie Herron (11)   27
Callum Middleton (11)   27
Ryan Brindley (11)   28

Cleves School, Weybridge

Natalie Strange (11)   28
Ashmeet Matharu (11)   29
Georgina Morris (10)   29
Gemma Pearce (11)   30
Toby Blyther (11)   30
Ryan Thompson (11)   31
James Hurton (11)   31
Dale Waters (11)   32
Bethany True (11)   33
Adham Mughal (11)   34
Georgina Clarke (11)   35
William Helliwell (11)   36
Josh Nicholls (11)   37
Amy Roberts (11)   38
Jennifer Grist (11)   39
Lois Holloway (10)   40
Alice Moxon (11)   41

Colley Lane Primary School, Halesowen

Drew Brown (9)	41
Abbey Byrne (9)	42
Matthew Taylor (8)	43
Chloe Edmonds (9)	44
Jack Ilic (9)	45
Ben Brettle (9)	46
Jonathan Shaw (9)	47
Pagan Locke (9)	48
Francis Brown (8)	49
Danielle Homer	50

Elmsett CE (VC) Primary School, Ipswich

Samuel Potter (8)	50
Chelsea Pratt (7)	51
James Robinson (10)	51
Zoe Griggs (8)	52
Sophie Demetriades (10)	52
Thomas Diduca (7)	53
George Mellor (7)	53
Matthew D'Souza (10)	54
Nathan Gull (10)	54
Adam Coleyshaw (10)	55
Sarah Stock (8)	56
Kitto Horsley (10)	56
Robert Moors (11)	56
Amy Coleyshaw (8)	57
Alice Diss (11)	57
Rachel Bridge (9)	57
Linzi Hill (8)	58
Sarah George (8)	58
Alistair Grant (7)	58
Harry Clark (7)	59
Amy Highland (8)	59
Lewis Kempson (8)	60

Harewood CE Primary School, Leeds

Felicity Emmott (9)	60
Rebekah Hooks (9)	61
Joshua Snaith (9)	61
Jake Harland (9)	62

Georgina Trifunovic (8)   63
Amelia Foote (9)   63
Saskia Lawson-Tovey (8)   64
Thomas Hartley (9)   64
Jodie Hullah (9)   65
Jasmine Nicholson (9)   65
Monica Rall (9)   66

Inverkeithing Primary School, Fife

Katie Walker (11)   66
Stuart Milne (8)   67
Holly Paterson (10)   67
Abbie Gardner (10)   67
Catherine Ostrom (11)   68
Colette Neill (8)   68
David Vaughan (10)   69
Rhiannon Cockburn (8)   69
Mercedes Black (8)   70
Colin Law (8)   70
Jamie Neil (10)   70
Claire Fairbairn (8)   71
Daniel Sinclair (8)   71
Graeme Anderson (10)   71
Kara Bradbeer (10)   72
Darren Paterson (10)   72
Holly Primrose (10)   72
Dayna Kernaghan (8)   73
Kieran Gear (8)   73
Emilly Campbell (8)   73
Samantha Buchanan (10)   74
Lauren Murie (10)   74
Demi Paterson (8)   75
Ben Wilkie (8)   75
Nathan Henderson (8)   75
Jade McKibben (8)   76
Adam Parsley (8)   76
Christopher Naughton (9)   76
Shona Briggs (8)   77

Newick CE Primary School, Newick

Francesca Thurston-Hobbs (7)	77
Charlotte Johnson (7)	77
Daniel Forster, Freddie Dean & Edward Minett (7)	78
Tanisha Marsh (7)	78
Rory Blackburn (7)	78
Sophie Hazel (7)	79
Amber Potter-Drake (7)	79
Edward Osborne (7)	79
Billy Benson & Kieran Eke (7)	80
Elizabeth Brown (6)	80
Connor Geary (7)	80
Ruby Shute (7)	81
William Davies (7)	81
Oliver Platt (6)	81
Georgina Thomas (6)	82
Rebecca England (7)	82
Aimee May (7)	82
Alice Gordon (7)	83
Kerri-Anne Clough & Rebecca Collins	83
Isabella Sachs (7)	84

Rayne Primary & Nursery School, Braintree

Natalie Reynolds (7)	84
Jordan Atkinson (7)	85
David Kukiewicz (10)	85
Charlie Clipson (10)	86
James Howard (10)	86
Mathew Howard (7)	87
Taylor-Rose Temperley (7)	87
Riley Baker (7)	87
Lily Arkwright (7)	88
Joshua Foster (7)	88
Connor Temperley (10)	89
Will Turner (7)	89
Georgi Addington Lees (7)	89
Max Turner, Harry Gordon & Jake Chitty (10)	90
Jordan Pitts (7)	90
Phil Carey (7)	91
Brooke Stevens	91
Megan Larkins (6)	92

Max Turner & Scott Preece (10)   92
Nikki Caton, Amy Ramessar & Gemma Wright (10)   92
George Arkwright & Fraser Ingram (10)   93
James Little (7)   93
Jack Webb & Ben Rawlings (10)   93
Ellan Ashton-Jones (7)   94

Sacred Heart Catholic Primary School, Barrow-in-Furness
Megan Peters (8)   94
Eden Smith (8)   94
Macaulay Murray (9)   95
John-Paul Byrne (8)   95
Megan Poole (9)   96
Chloe Macwhannell (9)   96
Jordan Wilkinson (9)   96
Glenn Elder (9)   97
Charlotte McDowell (9)   97
Tom Malkin (9)   97
Amie Atkinson (10)   98
Kieran Hackett (9)   98
Isabella McQuillan (8)   99
David Davies (10)   99
Daniel Griffin (8)   99
Liam McMillan (8)   100
Charlie Hillbeck (8)   100
Scott Foden (10)   100
Hannah High (8)   101
Curtis Rigg (10)   101
Ben Davies (10)   101
Ben Yorke (10)   102
Joshua Reay (10)   102
Kieran Miller (10)   103

Shirland Primary School, Alfreton
Abigail Earlie (11)   103
Lauren Minney (11)   103
Michael Ball (11)   104
Jack Marron (11)   104
Cassie Judson (11)   105
Louise McNaught (11)   105
Thomas Richardson (11)   105

Jacquii Brown (11)   106
Roxann Edwards (11)   106
Amie Shepperson (11)   107
Nathan Hadley (10)   107
Danny Gronbach (11)   107
Katie Walker (11)   108
Craig Ashmore (11)   108
Roseanna Foy (11)   109
Matthew Hubbard (11)   109
Leona Greaves (11)   109
Emma Basta (11)   110
Kieron Williams (11)   110
Luke Scott (11)   111
Lauren Wheatcroft (11)   111
Josie Jackson (11)   112
Mark Mildenhall (11)   112
Jennifer Worton (11)   113
Connor Hutchinson (11)   113
Sam Pywell (11)   114
Josh Morley (11)   114

South Wilford CE Primary School, Nottingham
Lucy Bugden (9)   115
Coral Parkes (9)   115
Anokhi Longia (9)   115
Connor Brindley (8)   116
Elizabeth Chadwick (8)   116
Isaac Marriott (9)   117
Amy Hughes (8)   117
Charlie Hopps (8)   118
Elizabeth Bowley (9)   118
Kirsty Barnes (9)   118
Shannon Taylor (8)   119
Megan Dexter (7)   119
Megan Elliott (7)   119
Tom Read (7)   120
Lauren Needham (9)   120
Katy Gamble (8)   121
Danielle Skermer (8)   121
Mollie Price (8)   122
Esther Rowe (9)   122

Macauley Robinson-Fisher (8)	123
Georgina Bird (9)	123
Shannon Pendergast (8)	124
Lianna Hastie (9)	124
Abbie Edmonds (8)	125
Thomas Hazledine (8)	125
Rhia Brindley (8)	126
Shauna Mullins (8)	126
Ellie Irvine (8)	126
Nicholas Belfitt (9)	127
George Alexander (9)	127
George Twiddy (8)	128

Turvey Lower Foundation School, Turvey

Harvey Fielden (6)	128
Robbie Williams (6)	128
Hayden Abeynaike (6)	129
Samantha Caine (6)	129
Annie Wallace (6)	129
Grace Venables (6)	130

Wendover CE Junior School, Aylesbury

Harry Price (9)	130

Whitestone Primary School, West Cross

Rhiannon Frayne (8)	130
Mitchell Drewson (9)	131
Ashleigh Richardson (8)	131
Ellie Ransome (8)	132
Adam Davies (8)	132
Emily Olsen (8)	132
Seren Noel (8)	133
Anna Bevan (8)	133
Cameron Bateman (8)	133
Peter Williams (8)	134
Abigail Gwynn (7)	134
Alys Worthing (9)	134
Bianca Lakkiss (9)	135
Tom Bowen (9)	135
David Allchurch (9)	136

The Poems

Basketball

I like to play basketball,
Jumping with the ball.
Bouncing and jumping,
To try and score points.

I am team captain,
My team isn't worried.
If we win or lose,
It's only a game.

We score loads of baskets,
More than the other team.
We do win, *yeah!*
Maybe we do care!

Amy Walsh (8)

Daydreaming

Miss O' Grady thinks I'm listening but I'm . . .
Scoring a free kick for England!
And celebrating all over the pitch.

Miss O' Grady thinks I'm writing but I'm . . .
Driving down the highway
In my Nissan Skyline Super Chip with Zack Ryan, Tom B and Tom S.

Miss O' Grady thinks I'm reading but I'm . . .
Getting Ronaldinho as my dad and
Tory Wilson as my mum.

Miss O' Grady thinks I'm joining in but I'm . . .
On stage rapping with 50 Cent,
Snoop Dogg, Eminem, Ice Cube and Dr Dre.

Liam Evans (10)

Weird

My little sister she is weird,
She sits around doing stuff.
She wears creepy clothes,
And she eats her chocolate puffs.

She rides around the neighbourhood,
She annoys my nan.
Gets called a little brat,
Mostly by my brother Dan.

Her name is Nina,
A pain in the neck.
Likes to go around and play,
Mainly on the deck.

Nina, she doesn't eat nice things,
A bottle of ketchup is her best.
Sugar in porridge,
What a pest.

Although Nina is weird,
She's my sister and that's what counts.
But above all she is funny,
That's no doubt.

Amanda Edwards (8)

Weather

Rain pours down all around you,
Sometimes it soaks you through,
The sun'll dry it up though,
So you won't have to get changed you know.

Wind is cold, very cold,
So wrap up warm when you're told,
But snow is colder, much, much colder,
Looks like you'll have to change after all!

Hailstones are hitting my conservatory roof,
Just like God's given them a hoof,
Thunder echoes all around,
Whilst lightning scorches all the ground.

Euan Dryburgh (10)

Roman Battle

The battle dragon did wail
Arrows like metal hail
Swords went clash
Armour went smash
Daggers went clang
Shields went bang
The Celts made a yell
As they fell
The spears flew higher
Houses were on fire
The Celts did run
The Romans had won!

James Dunsmore (8)
Baddow Hall Junior School, Chelmsford

Playground Poem

Playground, playground, nice and bright,
Playing round, in the light.
Running round, playing games,
No one calling people names!

Playing football on the field,
Always kicking someone's shield.
Playing tennis on the court,
People shading in the port!

On the field, very fast,
People running very fast.
Snakes and ladders, roll the dice,
Always people being nice!

The school is big, bits are small,
People running down the hall.
Get outside, quick, quick, quick,
To see my friend, very nice Mick!

Daniel Bury (10)
Baddow Hall Junior School, Chelmsford

Diaries

A diary is where you record things
A diary is where you have fun
A diary is where you keep secrets
From those lost loved ones.

Some pages are purple
Others are baby-blue
But most are really light pink
With a hint of my friends and you.

Now I must stop recording in my diary
Because my pages are red and fiery.

Jade Cooper (10)
Baddow Hall Junior School, Chelmsford

The Playground

Children run, shout and play,
All the time throughout the day.

Children run and play in the sun,
At snack time they sometimes eat a bun.

Children skipping round and round,
All the time till they fall to the ground.

People trying to mend a friend,
But it kind of drives them round the bend.

The grass is long, tall and green,
The children are never, never mean.

Boys play football really well,
When they score they run and tell.

When the girls come out to play,
They play catch and chase the boys away.

Now it is time for bed,
Let's look to another school day ahead.

Louisa Hill (8)
Baddow Hall Junior School, Chelmsford

Colours

Purple is my favourite colour
I look at it every hour
It shows up in lots of flowers.

Yellow, yellow like the sun,
Ice cream cones and a current bun.

Green, green, the grass is green
Open the door and look at the scene.

Then there is the rainbow
All the colours put together
How beautiful it is when it leaves the rain behind.

Sabrina Shales (10)
Baddow Hall Junior School, Chelmsford

Tigers

Tigers growl and tigers bounce
Tigers frown and then pounce
Tigers live on a mystery island
Where the birds sing
When the tigers want food they hunt for it and that thing.

So don't go where the tigers live
Otherwise they smell your meat
And then they come out roaring
Then you will soon find their clawing.

So when you're walking home one night
And you see a little paw
You might as well run
Because if it is a tiger
You wouldn't stand and hum.

Nicole Llewellyn (9)
Baddow Hall Junior School, Chelmsford

Time Travel

If you've been to the future, you'll know it's mad,
Some people good, but mostly bad.
If you've been to the past, you'll be sad,
It's better than the future so you'll be glad.
But our time now is all fine,
It's nice and shiny, beautiful and divine.

In the future everyone is stealing,
Those charity workers still appealing.
In the past the land was vast,
Today the buildings are popping up fast.

They had no beach,
But it's within our reach.
Now holidays are many,
But they don't cost a penny.

Joshua Glasson (10)
Baddow Hall Junior School, Chelmsford

Time Turner

I am going back in time,
I am singing a beautiful rhyme.
Now I am getting very close,
I am feeling the back of my toes.

Now I'm here but under control,
I have stolen a remote control.
I'm in prison under some bars,
I want to eat a bar of Mars.

Now I'm going back in the past,
Back to home at 5 and quarter past.
Going to bed as happy as can be,
But I think I left a part of me.

Dreaming of tomorrow
What will happen then?
Maybe I will go to the future
But that's tomorrow then.

Sophie Cole (10)
Baddow Hall Junior School, Chelmsford

Mother's Day

One day I went out to play
And forgot about Mother's Day.
I ran upstairs to get her present
But I don't think it was very pleasant.
When I found her she was sad
Now I'm getting very mad.
That night when I went to bed
Now listen carefully to what she said,
She said she loves me, like I love her
Now my cat is starting to purr,
I got her flowers colourful and bright
Now they will never go out of sight.

Bethany Llewellyn (9)
Baddow Hall Junior School, Chelmsford

Children's Stories

Once upon a time in a deep dark wood,
There lived a small girl named Red Riding Hood.
She slaughtered a wolf, oh what a beast
And then he was cooked for a tasty large feast!

Long ago in a gingerbread cottage
With all the sweets, within the rottage
Dear Hansel and Gretel pushed the witch in a fire
And they took her sweets, beyond their desire!

'Run, run, as fast as you can,'
This was said by the gingerbread man
He laughed and boasted and ran away
But was caught by the fox the very next day!

So if you're a child, retell these stories well
Do not let them get trapped in a shell
They once were the present, now they're the past
But these are just stories, that remain in our hearts.

James Raynal (10)
Baddow Hall Junior School, Chelmsford

Pictures In Clouds

Pictures in the clouds I see,
A lion, a bird and a bumblebee.
I love the pictures in the sky,
I see a dove flying high.

The sun is setting behind a cloud
Telling its stories, telling it to crowds.
Pictures in the clouds I see,
A lion, a bird and a bumblebee.

Tamara Anderson (9)
Baddow Hall Junior School, Chelmsford

Thank You Mum

Thank you Mum for being in my life
With the ups and downs and the worry and strife.

My friends come around and in comes my temper
I kick and scream until I feel better.

Mum comes in and sorts it out
Out goes my temper and in comes my doubt.

I say sorry, still wanting to kick
Or maybe throw a very large brick!

I go to my room feeling mad
But really I was very sad.

I'd climb out the window if I could
But I don't think that I really should.

As the time goes by
I'll sometimes cry.

But when Mum comes to see me after a while
We'll talk and we'll hug and end with a smile.

Emily Strudwick (9)
Baddow Hall Junior School, Chelmsford

Bullying

People that bully,
Are cruel and mean
They take the mick and hit and kick.

People that bully,
Make people sad
And call them silly crying lads.

People that bully,
Make people stay at home
When they are, they are alone.

Callum Hill (9)
Baddow Hall Junior School, Chelmsford

Football

There was once a ball that stood up tall,
The crowd were roaring,
That the player was boring.
The ball rolled away
And the player kept it in play,
The substitute cried, 'Can I come and play?'
Manager said, 'Wait another day.'
Someone went lame
In the game,

For every goal they score
They want more, more, more.
The players drive Mercedes Benz
But they never lend them to their friends.
The grass is green,
The players get mean,
The game gets tense
The pressure is immense.

Isaac Parker (9)
Baddow Hall Junior School, Chelmsford

The Plant

I'd been in town and just got home
When Mum dashed over to the phone
It was my aunt, she had a new plant
The guinea pig ate it
It really did hate it
And just in a tick
I'm sure it was sick
Green stuff, orange stuff
All over aunt Chris' walking stick!

William Watt (9)
Baddow Hall Junior School, Chelmsford

Playground Madness

In the playground it's complete, total madness,
Some people happy, others full of sadness.
Teachers telling off naughty children,
Children in the medical area.
Most children having fun,
Young infants crying, asking for their mum.

All the children play something different,
Some children like spinning tops,
Others like to play cops.
Boys always choose football,
Girls plan their trip to the shopping mall.

Lining up is the worst bit,
Playtime is over, oh no,
Back into the classroom, off we go.
Happy faces turn to glum faces,
Someone sad trips over his laces.
No more time in the playground today,
Tomorrow will bring another happy day
In the mad playground.

Vicky Cornforth (10)
Baddow Hall Junior School, Chelmsford

The Seasons

The river was flowing
The farmer was mowing
While it was snowing
The cricketers were throwing
And the flowers were growing.
The seasons are changing
The world is rearranging.

Josh Dodsley (10)
Baddow Hall Junior School, Chelmsford

The Playground

The children are playing,
All different things,
Football, netball,
Sticky toffee too!

The teachers are watching,
All different things,
Children, games
The lining up queue.

The birds are eating,
All different things,
Worms, beetles,
Crumbs they chew.

The sun is listening to
All different things,
The children laughing,
Till playtime's through.

Francesca Ross (10)
Baddow Hall Junior School, Chelmsford

Water Poem

Water, water all around
Droplets and their tapping sound.

Puddles rising, not surprising
Rain is going on.

Parents and babies singing songs
This shower is very long.

Grass is wet
Children upset.

The sun is finally up again.

Harriet Calland (9)
Chestnut Street CE Primary School, Sleaford

A New Life

Starting a new life
Can be very hard
Especially when you have to
Leave your friends behind.

I'm upset about leaving Clare
She's been the best ever friend
But now I have to move on
I think I'm going to cry.

I also have to leave my buddy
And that's very upsetting
Because she's been the best buddy
But I will get a new buddy.

I'm full of mixed feelings
Scared, nervous, excited as well
I've butterflies in my stomach
And I feel like I've had worms for tea.

Anxiety is swarming all over me
I'm curious about lessons
I sometimes walk about wondering
How much homework I will get.

Robyn Paige Tustain (11)
Chestnut Street CE Primary School, Sleaford

Friends

F riendship never ends
R acing through the bad times
I n the blue sky
E nd up in good times
N ever forget your friends
D etermined to keep them
S ailing through good times.

Harriet Rose Butcher (10)
Chestnut Street CE Primary School, Sleaford

Poppies

Poppies grow in the swaying grass,
For all those men who touched our hearts
Never forget it,
Or you'd regret it,
The 11th of November
Remember, remember.

Poppies were the first thing they saw
They were coming, more and more.
For all those men who had been,
By all people, poppies were seen.
The 11th of November
Remember, remember.

Sisters, brothers
Fathers, mothers
All had seen the flower, the odour of blood,
Poppies grow everywhere, even through the mud.
The 11th of November
Remember, remember, remember.

Emma Jackson (10)
Chestnut Street CE Primary School, Sleaford

The Shell That Lay By The Murky Waters

Dark and hard
Glows by night
People watch its shimmering light.

Bright and smooth
Dark and hard
It's so beautiful
It's hard to miss.

That's the poem of the
Shell that lay by
The murky water.

Holly Foxon (10)
Chestnut Street CE Primary School, Sleaford

An Unforgettable Time

Leaving primary,
Is an unforgettable time,
Starting secondary,
Is an unforgettable time,
An unforgettable time,
That will only happen once,
But will stay in your heart forever.

It fills you with:
Depression, sadness, tension
And many other emotions,
For many different reasons.

The emotions will go,
But the memory
Will be part of your life forever.

Friends will be lost
And great memories too,
But the sadness will be gone
After you make new friends
And be happy once again.

Macaulay Gibson (11)
Chestnut Street CE Primary School, Sleaford

Leaving School And Friends

I'm sad
I'm leaving
I'm curious about my friends
Will I ever see them again?

I'm scared
Will I make new friends?
I will be destroyed if I lose my friends
I'm terrified of starting my secondary school.

Luke George (11)
Chestnut Street CE Primary School, Sleaford

Starting Secondary School

I enter the classroom
My stomach aches
I look around
I feel down.

Who will I meet?
Who do I know?
How will people react to me?
Will I be the person people want me to be?

My nerves rise,
I go cold,
I sit down,
My teacher walks in,
And then it starts!

Jessica Williams (11)
Chestnut Street CE Primary School, Sleaford

Leaving School

I said bye-bye as I left the gates
I went to Coteland to make new mates
I wondered how I would get on,
Now everyone knows that I am gone.

I will be happy to go to school,
Some people think it's really, really cool,
I've been at Chestnut for years and years,
I've been achieving and got some cheers.

I'll say farewell and I will be sad,
I won't feel good, I'll feel so bad,
This is my school and I won't ever
Change my feelings about it.

Jordan Ashley Barrack (11)
Chestnut Street CE Primary School, Sleaford

Living A New Life

I shall miss my school
Losing friends
Feeling nervous about getting lost,
Making friends.

Friends are nice,
Hard to lose,
Don't want to leave.
Miss you a lot.

Knowing people
Is very good
Leaving friends
In a different form.

Leaving friends
Is very sad,
Miss them a lot
Leaving is tearful.

Clare Smith (11)
Chestnut Street CE Primary School, Sleaford

A Beginning!

I'm leaving school, I've been here too long,
I've had memories that I'll not forget
They are bubbling, screaming, crying and fading away
I am lost, my mates are falling behind me
But new ones are haunting me
Soon I won't know the old
They would have changed, everything would have changed
There isn't much time, I can't waste it
It's a new beginning so get ready
You're going down, right down.

Sophie Stokes (11)
Chestnut Street CE Primary School, Sleaford

Starting A New School

Starting my new school,
Leaving my old school,
Losing old friends,
Not knowing if I will make new ones,
Getting there at 9.00 am,
Starting a lesson when the bell rings,
Meeting my new teacher, saying hello,
I sit down in a place, waiting to start
I am worried a bit and I am *confused!*

Joshua Lack (11)
Chestnut Street CE Primary School, Sleaford

Leaving Primary School

Scared, horrid, nervous, upset
It's the last day of school
Leaving to go to secondary,
Saying goodbye to my friends.

Tears are coming out,
Everybody wanting to stay
A little longer, little longer
Then everyone goes, that is it.

Chloe Kirk (11)
Chestnut Street CE Primary School, Sleaford

Starting School

I'm nervous
I'm scared
I feel sick
My stomach churns
I feel like a lonely
Sheep stood in the field
The bell rings, I'm late.

Andrew Oglesby (11)
Chestnut Street CE Primary School, Sleaford

New Start!

The bell rang,
I put up my chair
Then I packed my bag
And walked out the door.

I walked
Across the playground
Then out of
The school.

Then something happened
I became a Year 7.

Lucy Smith (11)
Chestnut Street CE Primary School, Sleaford

Moving On

As we reach the end of school
The sadness will be growing
As our friends leave us
We shall leave them
As we move on
Our friends will move on
The sadness comes from saying goodbye
But we must move on.

Adam Billyard (11)
Chestnut Street CE Primary School, Sleaford

My Last Chance!

Every second that goes,
I get more and more scared
The fear builds up inside
Then it explodes like a
Volcano!

Tom Bannister (12)
Chestnut Street CE Primary School, Sleaford

Getting Ready

Excitement
When shopping on a weekend
For your school uniform;
Blazer,
Tie
And shirt.
Looking at the mobiles
Wishing I had one
Nokias
Sonys
And Motorolas.
In the stationary shop
Looking at the things;
Pen,
Pencil
And maths kit.

Adam Nicholls (11)
Chestnut Street CE Primary School, Sleaford

Leaving School!

A bit worried
Wondering what
The school
Will be like.

If it's horrible
Good, nice, cool
Pupils who like me.

I find out that
The school
Is good
And the pupils
Are cool.

Christian Lyth (11)
Chestnut Street CE Primary School, Sleaford

Questions

Leaving the school
I don't feel cool
Sad, sad, sad
I'm feeling sort of mad
I don't know why

I'm not glad I'm leaving this school,
Is secondary school cruel?
I don't know, I have so many questions.

Friends gone out of my life,
I want to chop another year in with a knife,
Remember, remember, remember,
I wish I was back in September,
I'm feeling tender,
Tonight at tea I hope school's not on the agenda.

I'm not glad I'm leaving this school,
Is secondary school cool?
I don't know, I have so many questions.

Lauren-Mae Pearson (11)
Chestnut Street CE Primary School, Sleaford

Starting Secondary School

I put on my blazer, tie, shirt, trousers and socks,
Will I make friends?
What will my school be like?
I am nervous.

My friend Harry is going to a different school
He is going to Carres, the boyo' grammar school,
I might never see him again.

My friend Jonathan is going to a different school,
He is going to Cotelands, the school in Ruskington
I might never see him again.
I hope I see them again.

Kathryn Cook (11)
Chestnut Street CE Primary School, Sleaford

First Steps

I entered the front gates,
Like an outsider,
I'm off to
Carres Grammar.

I enter the school
People say, 'Hi.'
I do up my tie
And straighten my blazer.

I enter

I smile, I take my seat
The lesson begins,
It's numeracy.

The bell rings
I grab my bag
I walk for the door
I'm out the door
I smile.

Harry Price (11)
Chestnut Street CE Primary School, Sleaford

Leaving And Starting

I will be sad to leave primary school
But happy to go to secondary school.
I will lose lots of friends,
But I will make new ones.
I will miss all the teachers,
But there will be new ones as well.
I will miss the interesting subjects,
But there will be more interesting ones in the future.

Shahin Jogi (11)
Chestnut Street CE Primary School, Sleaford

Leaving School!

Secondary school
Will be cool
Parting mates just
Drawl.

Leaving school,
Leaving mates,
Will I be different?
Will I make friends?

Is it just me
Who worries?
What will my
Teacher be like?
Will I be good enough?

I am nervous,
Is anyone else?
I am scared,
Will I get lost?

Sophie Rasen (11)
Chestnut Street CE Primary School, Sleaford

New School

I'm going to a new school
A bigger school
It will be so cool.

Will I meet new friends?
Will I like it?
My time at Chestnut Street has come to an end.

Year 6 has ended
Our time is done!

Claudia Taws (11)
Chestnut Street CE Primary School, Sleaford

An Ending And A Beginning

Leaving a family
Joining a new one
I'm curious, nervous and sad
Friends left behind,
New ones waiting,
I'm excited, happy, upset.

My primary gone,
Secondary school here,
I'm anxious, shy, apprehensive.
A new beginning,
An ending too,
I'm cheerful, proud, unhappy.

Harder work coming,
Easy is far behind,
I'm afraid, worried, ready,
My first day over,
Last day to come,
I'm content, joyful and having fun.

Katie Stalker (11)
Chestnut Street CE Primary School, Sleaford

Getting Ready

Getting ready on a Monday to go to secondary school,
Putting on my blazer, tie and shirt,
Feeling very nervous,
Forcing down my breakfast,
Cleaning my teeth quickly,
Getting in the car, looking at my watch,
Arriving at the gate,
Hoping I'm not late,
Going into my form,
Trying to make a good impression.

Tom Wiles (10)
Chestnut Street CE Primary School, Sleaford

New Clean Slate

Fear strickens
Fear tightens
Locked with a key
For me to never reach.

The gate is open
Once again
Sadness cries
All over again.

Big places
Busy people
Making me feel
Small and ignored.

Not yet settled
Will I ever be
Settled here?

Caycee Peskett-Hill (10)
Chestnut Street CE Primary School, Sleaford

Sad

Leaving my mates behind
Nervous, worried
Crying with sadness
Weeping, worried.

I'm cuddling my
Friends
They cuddle me too
I will miss them
They will miss me too.

I leave them behind
They leave me too
I cry my eyes out
I am scared.

Sean Riglin (11)
Chestnut Street CE Primary School, Sleaford

I'm Leaving School

I'm leaving school
I'm losing my friends
I'm getting nervous
I need their numbers quick.

Adam's going to Carres
The boys' grammar school
I might not see him again.

I'm leaving school
I'm losing my friends
I'm getting nervous
I need their numbers quick.

My girlfriend's going to
Girls' High
The girls' grammar school
I need to stay in touch.

I'm leaving school
I'm losing my friends
I'm getting nervous
I need their numbers quick.

I'm off to Saint George's
The college of technology
Two of my friends are in my form.

Nathan Williamson (11)
Chestnut Street CE Primary School, Sleaford

Volcano Of Fear

Fear bubbles
Anger
Why can't I be with my friends?
Loneliness overcomes me
No one likes me
Fear erupts into *happiness*
And it begins.

Elsie Machell (11)
Chestnut Street CE Primary School, Sleaford

Curious

I'm leaving primary for secondary
I wonder what it's going to be like,
We went to our new school,
Then went to the mall,
To buy our new clothes.

It's the last day of school,
Some people think it's cool,
I'm leaving Chestnut Street
But I'm going to meet
Some now people.

Leaving school
Starting school
Leaving friends
I'm curious

It's sad to see the last funny face,
And the multicoloured shoelace.

Katie Herron (11)
Chestnut Street CE Primary School, Sleaford

Leaving School

Leaving school
Is so cool,
Going to secondary school
Is so cool.

I'm top of the school,
I'm bottom of the school,
I'll miss my mates,
I'll keep some.

Leaving school
Is so cool,
Going to secondary school
Is so cool.

Callum Middleton (11)
Chestnut Street CE Primary School, Sleaford

New Beginning

It's nearly the month of September
I'm starting secondary school
It's called St George's and it's fun
My heart is ready to go to secondary
But my body wants me to stay
I like my friends and my teacher
I really don't want to go away
I've been at this school for 7 years
And I know my way around
And this is what I've got to say
I'm leaving, I'm sorry that I'm going
But you'll always be in my heart.

Ryan Brindley (11)
Chestnut Street CE Primary School, Sleaford

Teardrops

I lie in my bed and think of you
I'm trying to be strong
Holding your photo to my heart,
What we had is gone.

Looking back on our memories,
Despair trickles from my eyes,
I can see you never loved me,
You tricked me with your disguise.

I wished I hadn't met you,
That night you caught my stare,
How could I resist you?
How could I not care?

I don't want to believe it
My heart begins to drop
I would give anything,
To end the teardrops.

Natalie Strange (11)
Cleves School, Weybridge

The Ice-Breathing Dragon

There once was a dragon that was guarding some jewels,
People were trying to get in with tools,
Some were very rare,
In the dragon's lair.

He covered all the jewels with ice,
So there were no mice,
He rode around in an ice sledge,
Bumping into a massive hedge.

The hedge was very big,
And it was curly like a judge's wig,
The hedge had hurt him very bad,
That made him very mad.

He screamed out ice,
Shaped as dice,
He killed the hedge,
Then made a new sledge.

Ashmeet Matharu (11)
Cleves School, Weybridge

My Pussy Cat

My cat is as fat as he!
She also causes a big fee,
I think her coat is soft,
She likes to hide in the loft.

The favourite toy, a mouse,
I hate it when she eats woodlice.
Miaowing like a tiger,
Sometimes it's hard to find her.

When she tries to bite,
It's not very polite,
Her claws are very long,
Paws can be very strong.

Georgina Morris (10)
Cleves School, Weybridge

The Evil Teacher

My teacher is as evil as a creature,
But she is the only evil teacher.
She gives us homework when she gets cross,
When she gives out too much homework she goes over the top!

The beady eyes when she stares at us,
Her name is the evil Mrs Rush,
Her attitude when she is sleepy,
Can really be quite cheeky.

For dinner she has chicken stew,
She never wants to try anything new,
Her body is all round and fat,
Everybody complains about that.

But after all she is my teacher,
But the thing is . . .
She is an evil teacher!

Gemma Pearce (11)
Cleves School, Weybridge

Amish In The City

Here in the city,
It is alright.
Hanging with the city kids,
It is different from my country,
The Amish country.

All these gizmos and gadgets,
It's all very new,
But we don't use them in my country,
The Amish country.

Looking at the shops,
From Gucci to Louis Vuitton,
All these busy people,
Rushing and running around,
But not in my country.

Toby Blyther (11)
Cleves School, Weybridge

My Fire-Breathing Guinea Pig!

When I had my 5th birthday,
The one thing I wanted the most was,
A guinea pig, 'Hooorrraaayyy!'
After a month or so it stared going mad,
And then it started hibernating,
And I am really glad,
I started to forget about it,
I never really cared,
But now I'm really worried,
And very, very scared,
It started breathing fire on Tuesday afternoon,
I wish it never started,
I wish it would end soon!
It's burnt down the living room,
And all of upstairs too,
I think we're all coming to our doom!
I think it's getting better; it's burnt the postman and the post,
But now it's in the kitchen making all the toast!

Ryan Thompson (11)
Cleves School, Weybridge

My Family

My mum is mad and I love her very much,
My sister is horrid but quite cute!
My dad he snores a lot, oh boy!
My sister goes over the top sometimes.

My grandma and grandpa live in a big house,
Sometimes I stay thoro, I liko doing that,
Two cats called Tiger and Tarzan also live there
They spend all their days chasing a mouse.

James Hurton (11)
Cleves School, Weybridge

Mystery

Is there such a thing called Heaven,
Or is it just something to believe?
Was Jesus a good man,
Or was he a thief?

Is God an unknown creature,
Or is he what we think?
Is he a brown person,
Or is he really pink?

How does the world spin around,
Or does it spin at all?
Why doesn't gravity push us,
And why does it pull?

What happens to us when we finish,
Or do we just disappear?
Do we go to Hell,
Feeling full of fear?

Why are people like we are,
Or why are we all different?
Why are we all different,
When we could be the same?

Why do people cry,
When they can be cheerful and laugh? (Ha, ha, ha!)
Are people sensible,
On your behalf.

Who can say when you're being naughty,
They're not always well behaved,
Naughty children can kill,
Good children can save!

Dale Waters (11)
Cleves School, Weybridge

The Last Call

As I stare, I know that time is ending,
As I stare, I know that life's descending.

Even though the sun is rising,
I know that the blackness will come.
Soon enough for me the Earth will darken,
But brighten up for some.

Life is going by, slowly going past,
But even though I cannot hope, all my love will last.

As I lie here, I feel helpless, unwanted, alone,
Maybe God has left me, and instead left the darkness shown.

I think of my loved ones, the only happiness in my life,
I feel the pain of love; it's like my heart being torn by a knife.

I wonder what will happen to me, when I finally pass away,
Will I enter a new life, or lie in my grave day after day?

I start to want to leave the world, escape from the pain inside me,
But I'm afraid of what will happen after, I'll just have to wait and see.

Will there be anyone to guide me past the sadness,
Past the trickling tears?
Will there be anyone to guide me past all of my horrible fears.

I think of the questions, the questions that run through my head,
I try to relax, I try to be calm, I want to look peaceful when I'm dead.

Thinking of the happy memories, calmness is what I try to seek,
I know that the end is nearing, as tears trickle down my cheek.

I ignore the questions and think of my loved ones, them all,
As the darkness enters my eyes, this is my last call.

Bethany True (11)
Cleves School, Weybridge

Camp Nou

Driving up, parking against lots of cars,
As you enter through metal bars,
You see everyone shouting and cheering,
With the opposition being jeered.

The manager is giving the players last minute tips,
Looking over all the fans, finally get a glimpse
The match had kicked off, it was under way
The Barcelona keeper saves the ball to keep it at bay!

The atmosphere with everyone glued is amazing,
The match is action packed, you cannot stop gazing!
Deco with his pace is always running down the wing,
Ronaldinho with his skills is making the crowd sing!

Looking around you cannot see a single gap
Camp Nou is so big you would need a map!
Barcelona are in tremendously good form, they are 1st
Because they attack with fantastic bursts!

At the full-time whistle everyone leaves the ground,
And enters the jam-packed town
Everyone leaves, they're amazed at what they've seen
And to tell their friends where they've been!

Adham Mughal (11)
Cleves School, Weybridge

The Sea

I'm happy living by the sea,
It's the perfect place to be,
Staring at the shimmering waves,
Lashing at the ridged caves.

Tourists lounging, having fun,
Making the most of the glorious sun,
The beach is where the children play,
Laughing where the adults lay.

I'm not satisfied standing here,
My only company is a tear.
Rolling down my soft white cheek,
Out the window onto the cliff top peak.

All the creatures in the sea,
Seem to be living easily,
They've swam around from day-to-day
Ever since the end of May.

I guess I'm stuck up here forever,
The chance that I'll get out is never.
Stuck in this castle for the rest of my days,
Probably never changing my ways.

Georgina Clarke (11)
Cleves School, Weybridge

Granny From Hell

I have a granny,
Who's meaner than mean
She's got eyes like a hawk
And acts like a teen.

My granny is hard,
She can take the knocks,
This could be because,
She used to box.

If something goes wrong,
She blames it on me.
But if I complain,
I get no tea.

My granny wakes me up,
Just after dawn
I get so sleepy,
I'm too tired to yawn.

Apart from these things,
Of which there are many,
My big old granny
Is better than any!

William Helliwell (11)
Cleves School, Weybridge

Camp Nou

Barcelona have a lot of good history,
But their future success is a mystery.

Camp Nou smells of burgers and chips,
It is cold there so you might want to where mitts.

The view is amazingly fantastic,
Even though the seats were made of plastic.

Ronaldinho always running down the wing,
His skills are always his thing.

Eto'o Is always putting it away,
On his happy birthday.

In Barcelona it's so busy,
Ronaldinho makes me dizzy.

Their manager is truly amazing,
He can never stop gazing.

Deco with his long range shots,
Maxi Lopez with his fantastic blocks.

Barcelona is a really good team,
And they recruit at only 14.

They have won a lot of games,
And bought some famous names.

Josh Nicholls (11)
Cleves School, Weybridge

School Trip A-Z

A is for adventures

B is for bedtime in our dorms

C is for cows in the field opposite the site.

D is for ducks that swim in the pond.

E is for eating midnight feasts in the middle of the night.

F is for fantastic food, sometimes.

G is for going on the coach to travel.

H is for horses that we get to ride.

I is for indoor activities.

J is for jumping with excitement.

K is for kissing in the corridors.

L is for the leap of faith on the rope challenge.

M is for mice running around at night.

N is for nice teachers letting us stay up late.

O is for orienteering in the evening.

P is for pillow fights in the night.

Q is for queuing in the tuck shop.

R is for rope challenge that we all had fun on.

S is for socks left on the floor in the dorms.

T is for tea we had in the morning.

U is for umbrellas everybody had in their suitcase.

V is for vending sweets from the machine.

W is for wailing, not wanting to go home.

X is for xylophones that we played in music.

Y is for yachting that we did at the seaside.

Z is for the zoo we visited on the last day.

Amy Roberts (11)
Cleves School, Weybridge

The Garden A-Z

A dmired the beautiful butterflies
B ounced on the trampoline
C limbed up the sycamore
D ead-headed the pansies
E xamined the fish in the pond
F ollowed my dog up a tree
G rew some herbs
H id behind a bush
I nspected the vegetable patch
J umped on the weeds
K ept the lawn tidy
L ooked at nature all around me
M oved further up the garden
N oticed the apples on the trees
O pened a packet of seeds
P lanted some tulip bulbs
Q uarrelled with my brother
R ushed up the garden after a squirrel
S earched for my cat
T idied up afterwards
U ntied my shoelaces
V iewed the colourful birds in the sky
W ished that I hadn't made such a mess
e X plained why I was late for tea
Y awned after a hard day's work
Z oomed back inside the house.

Jennifer Grist (11)
Cleves School, Weybridge

The Moon

The moon shines down on my house, every night,
The reflections glowing down, that beautiful luminous light,
Bouncing off my roof, that radiant glimmering ball,
Sometimes it is like a wrong-way-round smile
And sometimes it's not there at all.

They say the moon's made out of cheese . . .
Edam, Cheddar or Stilton?
I like to go up there all right, though they would need a caution,
As all the astronauts would eat all of it,
There wouldn't be any left for me not even a little bit.

It reminds me, when it is whole,
Of a shimmering golf ball,
Being putted into a deep blue sky,
It's gone so far and so high.

Next time you look at our amazing moon,
You will see that soon,
The perspective is more dazzling than you thought,
More sparkling than a diamond you've ever bought.

Lois Holloway (10)
Cleves School, Weybridge

Bath Time

After tea is the time I dread
This happens before bed
Why do I have to be clean?
I hate it, my mum is so mean
But my mum gets me in anyway
It's a routine I do every day
The rubber duck goes drop
Making all the bubbles pop
In the water flows
Whilst in my head goes
As the soap slips
The water from the tap drips
In the water I sit
Getting clean, bit by bit.

Alice Moxon (11)
Cleves School, Weybridge

Cake And Chips

Cake
Cake
Cake and chips
Cake and chips
Cake and chips and lettuce
Cake and chips and lettuce dips
Dips
Dips
Lettuce dips
Cake and chips and lettuce dips
Chips
Chips
Cake and chips
Cake and chips
Cake
Cake
Cake and lettuce with a flake.

Drew Brown (9)
Colley Lane Primary School, Halesowen

Skipping Rhyme

Mars
Mars
Mars and Chomp
Mars and Chomp
Mars and Chomp and toffee
Mars and Chomp and toffee romp
Romp
Romp
Toffee and romp
Mars and Chomp and toffee romp
Chomp
Chomp
Mars and Chomp
Mars and Chomp
Mars
Mars
Mars

And chocolate sauce please!

Abbey Byrne (9)
Colley Lane Primary School, Halesowen

Skipping Rhyme

Toast
Toast and jam
Toast and jam
Toast and jam and chocolate
Toast and jam and chocolate spread
Spread
Spread
Chocolate spread
Toast and jam and chocolate spread
Jam
Jam
Toast and jam
Toast and jam
Toast
Toast
Toast

And

Cut up turkey please.

Matthew Taylor (8)
Colley Lane Primary School, Halesowen

Skipping Rhyme

Toast
Toast
Toast and jam
Toast and jam
Toast and jam and marg'
Toast and jam and creamy marg'
Marg'
Marg'
Creamy marg'
Toast and jam and creamy marg'
Jam
Jam
Toast and jam
Toast and jam
Toast
Toast
Toast

And

Hot bacon and egg.

Chloe Edmonds (9)
Colley Lane Primary School, Halesowen

Skipping Rhyme

Fish
Fish
Fish and beans
Fish and beans
Fish and beans and curry
Fish and beans and curry sauce
Sauce
Sauce
Curry sauce
Fish and beans and curry sauce
Beans
Beans
Fish and beans
Fish and beans
Fish
Fish
Fish

And

Chicken dippers please!

Jack Ilic (9)
Colley Lane Primary School, Halesowen

Skipping Rhyme

Toast
Toast
Toast and ham
Toast and ham
Toast and ham and chocolate
Toast and ham and chocolate spread
Spread
Spread
Chocolate spread
Toast and ham and chocolate spread
Ham
Ham
Toast and ham
Toast and ham
Toast
Toast
Toast

And

Coca-cola.

Ben Brettle (9)
Colley Lane Primary School, Halesowen

Skipping Rhyme

Cream
Cream
Cream and cake
Cream and cake
Cream and cake and chocolate
Cream and cake and chocolate spread
Spread
Spread
Chocolate spread
Cream and cake and chocolate spread
Cake
Cake
Cream and cake
Cream and cake
Cream
Cream
Cream

And

Roly-poly please!

Jonathan Shaw (9)
Colley Lane Primary School, Halesowen

Skipping Rhyme

Cake
Cake
Cake and custard
Cake and custard
Cake and custard and chocolate
Cake and custard and chocolate spread
Spread
Spread
Chocolate spread
Cake and custard and chocolate spread
Custard
Custard
Cake and custard
Cake and custard
Cake
Cake
Cake

And

Jammy Dodgers please!

Pagan Locke (9)
Colley Lane Primary School, Halesowen

Skipping Rhyme

Beans
Beans
Beans and toast
Beans and toast
Beans and toast and grated
Beans and toast and grated cheese
Cheese
Cheese
Grated cheese
Beans and toast and grated cheese
Toast
Toast
Beans and toast
Beans and toast
Beans
Beans
Beans

And

Barbecue sauce please!

Francis Brown (8)
Colley Lane Primary School, Halesowen

Skipping Rhyme

Toast
Toast
Toast and jam
Toast and jam
Toast and jam and turkey
Toast and jam and turkey cold
Cold
Cold
Turkey cold
Toast and jam and turkey cold
Jam
Jam
Toast and jam
Toast and jam
Toast
Toast
Toast

And

Tomato sauce please!

Danielle Homer
Colley Lane Primary School, Halesowen

My Friend
(Based on 'The Furniture Game' by Sandy Brownjohn)

This person is a bumpy chair.
He is like a lively gorilla.
His colour is a bubbling red.
He is an annoying drum.
He is Tesco on a hot day.
If he were a food he would be finger-licking lamb chops.
He is a delicious drink of apple juice.
He is a cheerful chatterbox.

Samuel Potter (8)
Elmsett CE (VC) Primary School, Ipswich

School

In school I like:
Reading poems,
Cooking fairy cakes,
Writing letters,
Helping others,
Making models,
Thinking thoughts,
But
I don't like:
Sitting still,
Keeping quiet,
Drawing pictures,
Counting things,
Taking away and
I don't like boring games.

Chelsea Pratt (7)
Elmsett CE (VC) Primary School, Ipswich

The Tree

I look very good in the snow
I am not a tall tree, I am low
I have birds on my twigs
Few of them that are big,
I have big long roots,
They plunder and meander,
Through the ground like a hundred boots
I am not a young tree
I am old but my leaves on my branches still hang free
I always get to see the sunset
Because I live in Elmsett.
I have a beautiful silver coat
It floats through the air like a boat,
Have you guessed what tree I am, oh well,
That's for me to know, you to find out.

James Robinson (10)
Elmsett CE (VC) Primary School, Ipswich

If I Were A Tree

If I were I tree I would love to
Go on holiday with my friends
If I were a tree I would love to go swimming
If I were a tree I would dislike kids pulling off my bark
If I were a tree I would like to talk to animals.
If I were a tree I would like to
Tell people what it's like to be a tree.
If I were a tree I would dream
About what happened last year.
If I were a tree I would dislike birds nesting in my branches
If I were a tree I would hate a woodpecker pecking at me
If I were a tree it would tickle me
If a ladybird ran across me
If I were a tree I would like people taking pictures of me.

Zoe Griggs (8)
Elmsett CE (VC) Primary School, Ipswich

The Wonderful Weeping Tree

Gentle drifting looking lady,
Flowing, rustling in the pleasant breeze,
Her blossoming yellow green leaves drooping down low,
Her tiny yellow flowers blossoming over night,
Her long wavy hair all twisted, flowing through the air,
She has a towering tall shadow,
She weeps over rivers and streams,
But makes sure she's still tall and not small
So she stands out from all the rest.
I wonder if you've guessed yet,
It's the wonderful weeping willow looking her very best.

Sophie Demetriades (10)
Elmsett CE (VC) Primary School, Ipswich

Dragon Birth

(Based on 'Dragonbirth' by Judith Nicholls)

In a ghostly graveyard
Of long ago
There stood a gravestone
Beneath the gravestone
There was a cave
Inside the cave there was
A big dark hole
Inside the hole
There was an egg
Inside the egg there was
A crack
Out of the crack
Came a foot
Then a head
Then a leg
Then a *dragon!*

Thomas Diduca (7)
Elmsett CE (VC) Primary School, Ipswich

School

In school everybody
Is writing poems
Helping others
Adding numbers
Thinking thoughts
Drawing pictures
Making models

And everybody
Likes doing that.

George Mellor (7)
Elmsett CE (VC) Primary School, Ipswich

The Mystery Tree

As silent as snow
On a soft winter day,
Its branches long and slim
While going astray,
Leaves like a heart
Crinkled up dead,
Bark just like planks,
Rough, thin and red.
As twisted as twigs,
On a red hot fire,
Gliding in the wind
Like an old town crier,
Smells of nothing
But strangely quite nice,
Home to insects,
Spiders and lice,

That's all we know
But you're not sure
I'll tell thee,

Yes it's the mystery tree!

Matthew D'Souza (10)
Elmsett CE (VC) Primary School, Ipswich

Resemblance

The deadwood tree is now evil indeed,
His evil needs will forever be greed,
The peeling bark clings for its life,
This sin-ridden tree sees his knife,
This murderous fiend disposes of his leaves,
But for the moment no creature seems to grieve,
Our evil-doing tree still grows so high,
As the greed still tries to reach for the sky.

Nathan Gull (10)
Elmsett CE (VC) Primary School, Ipswich

The Growing Tree

In the green, green meadow,
By a murky stream,
A tree is growing in a dream
And slowly, slowly,
The branches show their wonderful buds.

In the green, green meadow,
By a murky stream,
A tree is growing in a dream
And slowly, slowly,
The branches show their lovely leaves.

In the green, green meadow,
By a murky stream,
A tree is growing in a dream
And slowly, slowly,
The branches show their beautiful blossom.

In the green, green meadow,
By a murky stream,
A tree is growing in a dream
And slowly, slowly,
The branches show their juicy fruit.

In the green, green meadow,
By a murky stream,
A tree is growing in a dream
And slowly, slowly,
The branches show their silky seeds.

In the green, green meadow,
By a murky stream,
A tree is growing in a dream
And slowly, slowly,
The ground proudly shows its youngest ever tree.

Adam Coleyshaw (10)
Elmsett CE (VC) Primary School, Ipswich

Someone I Know

(Based on 'The Furniture Game' by Sandy Brownjohn)

This person is a jolly monkey
If she were a colour
She would be soft mauve.
She's a very shiny brass trombone
If she were a meal she
Would be mouth-watering pasta.
She's icy water on a scorching hot day
She is a far off country village
She is a comfortable armchair.

Sarah Stock (8)
Elmsett CE (VC) Primary School, Ipswich

Winter

Winter always gives me a good feeling inside
With tiny snowflakes on the windows,
Snowmen dotting the countryside.
Warm mugs of hot chocolate,
Snowball fighting in the streets,
Children all wrapped up in scarves and bobble hats.
Snow covered trees glistening in the sun,
I love winter.

Kitto Horsley (10)
Elmsett CE (VC) Primary School, Ipswich

The Bijou Tree

Down the great field in a group of big trees,
There is one tree that seems scared,
It has sad cracky bark looking like a crying face,
It has a great smile of blossom too though,
It has some spikes like weapons on its branches,
The tree may be there till it gets blown down one day.

Robert Moors (11)
Elmsett CE (VC) Primary School, Ipswich

This Person Is

(Based on 'The Furniture Game' by Sandy Brownjohn)

This person is a jolly monkey
He is a gigantic drum
If he were a fruit
He would be a ripe juicy peach.
He reminds me of jacket potatoes
He is icy water on a hot day
If he were a place
He would be a snowy mountain.

Amy Coleyshaw (8)
Elmsett CE (VC) Primary School, Ipswich

The Twisted Tree

The small, twisted, leaning tree,
Stands between the other trees,
With tiny, little, berry leaves,
And insect hiding underneath.

The little, twisted, curving tree,
Stands within a pile of leaves,
With zigzagging branches like spiders' legs,
And also woodworm inside its chest.

Alice Diss (11)
Elmsett CE (VC) Primary School, Ipswich

Questions To A Tree

What is it like to be a tree?
Is it hard to find food?
Does it hurt when woodpeckers peck at you?
What is it like when people come and sit under you?
What is it like to be outside all the time?
What is it like when kids climb on you?
Do you still want to be a tree?

Rachel Bridge (9)
Elmsett CE (VC) Primary School, Ipswich

A Friend

(Based on 'The Furniture Game' by Sandy Brownjohn)

This person reminds me
Of a bouncy Jack Russell
If she were a colour
She would be bright blue
If she were a food
Se would be Kentucky Fried Chicken
She is a soft armchair
If she were a place
She would be Hadleigh on a scorching hot day.

Linzi Hill (8)
Elmsett CE (VC) Primary School, Ipswich

If She Were

(Based on 'The Furniture Game' by Sandy Brownjohn)

If she were a colour
She would be a dark blue.
She reminds me of a garden.
If she were food
She would be a chicken nugget.
She reminds me of a bouncy bed,
If she were a musical instrument
She would be a beautiful guitar.

Sarah George (8)
Elmsett CE (VC) Primary School, Ipswich

A Tree Dreams

A tree dreams of flying as fast as Concorde
A tree dreams of going to school.
A tree dreams of driving a racing car.
A tree dreams of being the richest man in the world.
A tree dreams of being the biggest in the forest.
What would we do without a tree?

Alistair Grant (7)
Elmsett CE (VC) Primary School, Ipswich

School

At school I like:

Adding up
Taking away
Playing games
Making models
Cooking buns
And using the laptop.

But
I don't like
Sitting still and
Literacy.

Harry Clark (7)
Elmsett CE (VC) Primary School, Ipswich

Birth Of A Dragon

(Based on 'Dragonbirth' by Judith Nicholls)

In the darkest depths
Of long ago
There stood a terrifying tree
Surrounded by stinging nettles
Inside that tree
There was a hole
In that hole there lay an egg
In the egg there was a crack
From the crack came a flame
In the flame
There was a dragon!

Amy Highland (8)
Elmsett CE (VC) Primary School, Ipswich

This Morning
(In the style of M Rosen)

'I can see you Lewis'
'Bang! Bang!'
'Stop it Lewis'
'Mum, Lewis keeps shooting at me'
'Well he's a silly boy. Get in the car.'
'That's my side'
'No it's not'
'Yes it is so'
'You two stop it!'

Lewis Kempson (8)
Elmsett CE (VC) Primary School, Ipswich

In The Attic

In the attic I will find . . .

An old, smooth velvet cloak that has been lost
For millions of years.

In the attic I will hear . . .

The sound of wriggling, revolting rats
Running around my great grandad's army trunk.

In the attic I will touch . . .

An old worn-out teddy that my mum used to cuddle,
It could be worth millions of pounds.

In the attic I will smell . . .

The smell of my grandma's special blueberry cake
Because she used to cook in my attic.

In the attic I will taste . . .
Old grubby dust that has been scattered everywhere.

Felicity Emmott (9)
Harewood CE Primary School, Leeds

Under My Bed

Under my bed I will see,
A spider from under the sea,
As tall as a bush,
But that will never be.

Under my bed I will hear,
A roar as loud as an alarm,
From a ferocious lion.

Under my bed I will touch,
A blob of green paint to make my arm green,
And It will make me look like an ogre,
And turn me green.

Under my bed I will smell,
A pile of old smelly socks,
That has been there for a week.

Under my bed I will taste,
An old burger that has just come today.

Rebekah Hooks (9)
Harewood CE Primary School, Leeds

Under My Bed

Under my bed I will see a
Dusty doorway to a distant land.

Under my bed I will taste dust
Like lots of flies flying into my mouth.

Under my bed I will smell a dragon's breath
Breathing on me like a match is being extinguished.

Under my bed I will touch
A golden feather from an eagle.

Under my bed I will hear the pipes
Dripping like a wolf's saliva dripping.

Joshua Snaith (9)
Harewood CE Primary School, Leeds

In The Attic

In the attic I will find . . .

A wriggly giggly rat, a pile of golden dust
As big as a baby rabbit
And a huge pile of battered
And rusty bars of metal.

In the attic I will hear . . .

A pair of mice squeaking to each other
Like people screaming.
A rotten old Christmas tree's leaves
Falling gently to the ground.

In the attic I will see . . .

An old wooden chest and old broken soft teddy bears.
I will see broken glass that is small
Sparkling and shining in a hole in the roof.

In the attic I will touch . . .

A jar of sharks' teeth
All different sizes
I will touch an old Japanese learning book with holes in it.

In the attic I will smell . . .

A rotten tree's leaf and the smell of smoke.

Jake Harland (9)
Harewood CE Primary School, Leeds

On The Beach I Will Find . . .

On the beach I will find
Nice yellow patterns on shells in my hands.

On the beach I will see
Blue waves crashing into the smooth soft sand.

On the beach I will hear waves,
And children playing and jumping the waves.

On the beach I will feel
Soft smooth sand in-between my toes.

On the beach I can smell
Salty seawater.

On the beach I can taste
Yellow sand tickling my throat like a chocolate bar.

Georgina Trifunovic (8)
Harewood CE Primary School, Leeds

Under My Bed

Under my bed I will see . . .
Big and small objects
Stood still like statues of buildings.

Under my bed I will hear . . .
The tap of spiders' feet
As they hurry across the floor.

Under my bed I will smell . . .
Dust, which has gathered up over the years.

Under my bed I will touch . . .
Hard dusty books and spiders' webs
Which are crumbling up into tiny pieces.

Under my bed I will taste . . .
Cold air and dust which
Has mixed together to make it taste horrible.

Amelia Foote (9)
Harewood CE Primary School, Leeds

In The Attic

In the attic I will see . . .
An old, wooden, antique rocking chair, covered in dust
With lots of woodworm crawling about in it.

In the attic I will hear . . .
Big, black vampire bats flying about looking
For the big, brown scampering rats to eat
Who are looking for cushions to nibble at.

In the attic I will touch . . .
Small, white sleeping mice that send shivers
Down my spine when they squeak or scamper away.

In the attic I will smell . . .
Old, rotting, dusty wood that has been snapped
From an old, oak staircase.

In the attic I will taste . . .
Horrible, old dust streaming into my mouth
With lots of dust mites.

Saskia Lawson-Tovey (8)
Harewood CE Primary School, Leeds

In The Attic

In the attic I will find . . .
A blood-sucking spider, which is as blind as a bat.

In the attic I will find . . .
The sound of a rat squirming through my legs.

In the attic I will touch . . .
The silkiness of a ghost's white sheet.

In the attic I will smell . . .
The dust floating around me.

In the attic I will taste . . .
A bat's hairy black small legs.

Thomas Hartley (9)
Harewood CE Primary School, Leeds

In The Attic

In the attic I will see a
Golden glittering gleam of a lock.
A silky slippery ledge of a piece of a silk sari.
A piece of wood like the vein of a leaf.

In the attic I will hear the sweet small squeal of a baby bat.
The blast of a balloon like the shot of a gun going off.

In the attic I will touch an old bath toy that had snapped in half.
An old bag in tatters.
A mouldy wig and rat skin.

In the attic I will smell a mouldy piece of moss
Like a sea splashing against the shore.

In the attic I taste a million mouldy sweets.
If you ever go into your attic you might see all these things.

Jodie Hullah (9)
Harewood CE Primary School, Leeds

On The Beach I Will Find

On the beach I will see . . .
A crab's shell as smooth as a computer screen.

On the beach I will hear . . .
A boat crashing on the mossy rocks.

On the beach I will touch . . .
The green, slimy seaweed under my toes.

On the beach I will smell . . .
The salty sea crashing under my feet.

On the beach I will taste . . .
The oily fish coming towards my pink lips.

Jasmine Nicholson (9)
Harewood CE Primary School, Leeds

In The Attic

In the old spooky attic I will taste . . .

The taste of dirty, dark dust which has been
Lying on the creaky floorboard for years and years.

In the old spooky attic I will hear . . .

Black rats scratching and scurrying like a witch's cat
Sharpening its nails on the old pieces of sandpaper.

In the old spooky attic I will smell . . .

The smell of an old, wrinkly, warty, black witch's heart.

In the old spooky attic I will touch . . .

A big yellow spider, which is about to eat its prey.

In the old spooky attic I will find . . .

An old raggedy black book called 'The Witches' Spells'.

Monica Rall (9)
Harewood CE Primary School, Leeds

Miller

I have a dog called Miller
He isn't a killer,
He is a boxer,
He wants to be a pop star
As well as a rock star.
Miller's fast he will go past like a rocket,
You can't put him in your pocket.
His friend is Wendy
She's really, really trendy,
And very, very friendly.

Katie Walker (11)
Inverkeithing Primary School, Fife

Crocodile

Crocodile
Fierce, has a spiky back
Green
Swims and walks
Finds food
Is wriggly and angry
Lives in rivers, zoos and the jungle
Chomping greedily
Fierce, with a spiky back
Crocodile.

Stuart Milne (8)
Inverkeithing Primary School, Fife

My Cat

I found a cat all alone,
It adopted us and our home,
I found it was abandoned and had no home,
It was just a kitten,
We saw no signs for a lost kitten.
It's very happy now it's being fed,
It's not looking for a home anymore!

Holly Paterson (10)
Inverkeithing Primary School, Fife

Friends

Friends forever, that's who we are,
It's too bad I support the pars.
Friends forever, that's what we are
None of us are into cars.
Friends forever, that's who we are.

Abbie Gardner (10)
Inverkeithing Primary School, Fife

Seasons

Winter, white winter,
See the robins chirping.
Winter, white winter,
Watch the snowfall.

Spring, spring, zingy spring,
Watch the blossom drop.
Spring, spring, zingy spring,
Look, flowers are peeking.

Summer, sunny summer,
Crops are drying.
Summer, sunny summer,
Everyone is getting sunburnt.

Autumn, amazing autumn,
Red and yellow leaves.
Autumn, amazing autumn,
Trees are going bare.

Catherine Ostrom (11)
Inverkeithing Primary School, Fife

Crocodile

Crocodile
Green, long
Slithers, swims underwater
Walks, flicks its tail
Lives in a swamp or zoo
Humans taste good!
Green, long
Crocodile.

Colette Neill (8)
Inverkeithing Primary School, Fife

Chompy

I have an imaginary friend,
Who likes to jump and play,
He cares about his trend,
With me he will always stay.

Chompy is he,
I like him so,
He's always happy,
With no woe.

I have such fun,
Along with a muddle of hats,
We usually watch 'Naked Gun',
And other things like that.

Chompy is a goat,
With a water keg,
His cry is like a bleat,
Sometimes I don't know if he begs.

David Vaughan (10)
Inverkeithing Primary School, Fife

Dolphin

Dolphin
Grey, smooth
Swims, leaps
Fast dives
In the ocean
Quickly eating fish
Grey, smooth
Dolphin.

Rhiannon Cockburn (8)
Inverkeithing Primary School, Fife

Chimpanzee

Chimpanzee
Powerful, hairy
Plays and scratches a lot
Swings, walks
Lives in the jungle and zoo
Loves ripe fruit
Powerful, hairy
Chimpanzee.

Mercedes Black (8)
Inverkeithing Primary School, Fife

Whale Shark

Whale shark
Strong but harmless
Swims, calls
Darts and skims
In the ocean
Swallows mackerel fast
Strong but harmless
Whale shark.

Colin Law (8)
Inverkeithing Primary School, Fife

Football

I like playing football,
I like scoring goals,
My favourite teams are Arsenal and Celtic,
And I'm very good at playing football.

Jamie Neil (10)
Inverkeithing Primary School, Fife

Koala

Koala
Fur grey
Climbs, swings
Crawls, carries babies in pouch
Lives in the outback in Australia
Eats leaves and green plants
Cute, wild
Koalas.

Claire Fairbairn (8)
Inverkeithing Primary School, Fife

Mountain Lions

Mountain lion
Furry, scary
Roars, scares
Leaping, sneaking
Mountains are its home
Eats other animals
Furry, scary
Mountain lion.

Daniel Sinclair (8)
Inverkeithing Primary School, Fife

My Animal

I got a new cat, its name was Fred,
And it was very red.
He liked bread but most of all,
He liked his bed in his little shed.

Graeme Anderson (10)
Inverkeithing Primary School, Fife

The Voice Of The Rainforest

I give you air but what do you give me?
Destruction.
I give you medicines but what do you give me?
Destruction.
I give you beautiful creatures but what do you give me?
Destruction.
I give you nature and beauty but what do you give me?
Destruction.
I give you my today but what about your tomorrow?

Kara Bradbeer (10)
Inverkeithing Primary School, Fife

Menace Friend

I once had a friend who was a menace
He was crazy about tennis
It got on my nerves
He had lots of verve
That's the menace
And his name was Dennis
That's all about Dennis the tennis menace.

Darren Paterson (10)
Inverkeithing Primary School, Fife

Voice Of The Rainforest

You chop me down when I give you life,
You burn me when I give you medicine.
I am beautiful,
I give you nature but you destroy me.
Now what will there be for your children?
All my animals will be gone.
Do you want that?

Holly Primrose (10)
Inverkeithing Primary School, Fife

Rabbit

Rabbit
Fluffy, cute
Jumps, runs
Hopping fast
Hutch, meadows, burrows
Nibbling carrots, cucumber and grass
Fluffy and cute
Rabbit.

Dayna Kernaghan (8)
Inverkeithing Primary School, Fife

Snake

Snake
Slimy, poisonous
Crawls, bites
Slithers smoothly
Lives in deserts and under rocks
Eating mice
Slimy, poisonous
Snake.

Kieran Gear (8)
Inverkeithing Primary School, Fife

Rabbit

Rabbit
Hopping, running
Jumping
In its hutch
Nibbling grass and rabbit food
Twitching whiskers and nose
Hopping, running
Rabbit.

Emilly Campbell (8)
Inverkeithing Primary School, Fife

Voice Of The Rainforest

I give you life
I give you health
But in return you cut me down.
So lovely
So bright
Until you come and spoil the night.
Birds squawking all day long
Pumas running fast and strong.
A sloth sliding down the tree
As lazy as can be.
I am starting to wonder
If there will be any
Rainforests left at all.

Samantha Buchanan (10)
Inverkeithing Primary School, Fife

Voice Of The Rainforest

I give you oxygen
I give you shelter
And in return you chop me down.
Why do you do it?
You are greedy people.
To be rich and wealthy you destroy the beauty.
You destroy the life that is now no more.
I was big and strong but now am weak and shrivelled.
When will you stop, or will you ever?

Lauren Murie (10)
Inverkeithing Primary School, Fife

Frog

Green with strong legs
Hops, swims
Jumps, dives
In watery places
Eating flies
Green with strong legs
Frog.

Demi Paterson (8)
Inverkeithing Primary School, Fife

Tiger

Stripy, sneaky
Hunts, hides
Runs, pounces
In the jungle wild
Meat eater
Stripy, sneaky
Tiger.

Ben Wilkie (8)
Inverkeithing Primary School, Fife

Brown Bear

Brown bear
Big, fierce
Climbs, sleeps
Climbs up and down
It lives in forests
Eats leaves
It's brown and scary
Brown bear.

Nathan Henderson (8)
Inverkeithing Primary School, Fife

Horses

Horses
Strong smooth
Fast running
In countryside fields
Slowly chomping grass
Strong, smooth
Horses.

Jade McKibben (8)
Inverkeithing Primary School, Fife

Rhino

Rhino.
Two horns, little tail.
Strong, powerful.
Charges, stomps,
Lives in the zoo, Africa and Asia.
Is a vegetarian, eats fruit and veg.
Is fast and cool.
Rhino.

Adam Parsley (8)
Inverkeithing Primary School, Fife

Polar Bear

Polar bear
White, furry
Swimming and swimming
Hunting and fishing
Eating fish and seals
Strong and friendless
White, furry
Polar bear.

Christopher Naughton (9)
Inverkeithing Primary School, Fife

Fish

Fish
Silvery, small
Swims and eats
Wriggles, dives
Eats fish food
Has fins and gills
Fish.

Shona Briggs (8)
Inverkeithing Primary School, Fife

Bread

Sweet, spicy ginger cake squidging in my mouth.
Black bread rolls rolling in my mouth.
Crumbly toast crunching in my mouth.
French sticks, crunch sticks, nice.
Ice cream, freezing.
Juicy grapes, refreshing, watery.
Soft rolls squidging in my mouth.
Sandwiches going hard in the sun.
Bubbly lemonade fizzy when I pour it.

Francesca Thurston-Hobbs (7)
Newick CE Primary School, Newick

Poem About A Seaside

Horses swimming in the water
And waves, the wavy sea
Splashing people body boarding
Blue is for the sea
Green is for seaside weed
The sand feels smooth
The sea came alive long ago.

Charlotte Johnson (7)
Newick CE Primary School, Newick

The War

The war! The war!
The wind is blowing loud
And soldiers have no food.
I feel sick and the door is swinging
And I hear pain when helping people
The people are dying and I am in danger
Bombs exploding.
Bayonets stabbing at my body
Freezing cold
The rain hits the wind
Dripping blood, I am losing life
Final thoughts of my loving family
Terrified I might never see them again
Goodbye! Goodbye!

Daniel Forster, Freddie Dean & Edward Minett (7)
Newick CE Primary School, Newick

My Ruby Ring

My ruby ring was red and shiny.
Every time I looked at it, it made me smile.
When I was going out for a walk it fell,
Out of my colourful pocket.
I am now really, really sad that I lost it.
I feel lonely without it.

Tanisha Marsh (7)
Newick CE Primary School, Newick

Shark

Sounds like slashing of the teeth.
Tastes like death surrounds you as the teeth dig into flesh.
Smells like rotting fish.
Looks as if it flies like a bird.
Feels as smooth as a rubber that has been stretched.

Rory Blackburn (7)
Newick CE Primary School, Newick

Bonfire Food

Sticky, gooey marshmallows roasting over the fire,
Sizzling sausages frying in a pan,
Juicy beefburgers on the barbecue,
Spicy hot dogs cooling down,
Roasted chestnuts being sold,
Fizzy beer being drunk,

Soothing warm milk settling me down.

Sophie Hazel (7)
Newick CE Primary School, Newick

My Grandad Is Lost

My great, great grandad gave me presents.
And took me to the park.
He was fun and made me happy.
I remember the night my mum and dad told me he was dead.
I felt very sad.
And I felt very uncomfortable.
And I cried.

Amber Potter-Drake (7)
Newick CE Primary School, Newick

Crimean War

Cold,
Terrifying,
Pain,
Danger,
Noisy,
Anxious,
Dying alone,
Boom!
Silence, then death.

Edward Osborne (7)
Newick CE Primary School, Newick

Poem About A Dying Soldier

Shivering,
Terrifying gunfire.
Devastating,
Death and dying.
Battlefield,
Stained red with blood.
Squelching,
Muddy boots.
Screaming,
Pain and terror.
Friendship,
Comfort the dying.

Billy Benson & Kieran Eke (7)
Newick CE Primary School, Newick

Horses

The sound of the clattering hooves
I feel as happy as a flower
I feel as happy as sunlight
Horses sweet as sticky toffee
The canter will turn to a gallop
I feel dizzy and happy.

Elizabeth Brown (6)
Newick CE Primary School, Newick

Food

Crunchy carrots
Bumpy cauliflower as white as snow.
Sweetcorn yellow as the sun.
Broccoli looking like trees in the forest.

Connor Geary (7)
Newick CE Primary School, Newick

Seaside

The seaside people body boarding and swimming.
Children playing and making sandcastles.
The seaside people swim in the sea.
People diving,
Sea horses swimming for fish.
Children having fun.
Crowds of people.
People hot.
People bathing.
The sea is blue and green.
Making me feel as hot as the sun.
Waves rough and swooshing
The sea came alive long ago.

Ruby Shute (7)
Newick CE Primary School, Newick

Sea Life

Seals, fish or sharks live in the sea
And are many different colours
Whales are mammals
But are still sea creatures.

William Davies (7)
Newick CE Primary School, Newick

My Lost Mouse

Nibbles was dark green with black spots.
I thought she was really cute.
I was playing at school, I put Nibbles down
And when I looked back she was gone.

Oliver Platt (6)
Newick CE Primary School, Newick

Green Turtle

Mean turtle

Bare turtle
Cold turtle
Cool turtle
Mad turtle
Stripy turtle
Wet turtle

No way a shark can crunch a turtle's shell.

Georgina Thomas (6)
Newick CE Primary School, Newick

My Doll

My doll was Maggie.
I was in a shop and I put her on a chair
When I came back she was gone.
I felt very, very sad indeed.
I tried to find her but I could not.
And I feel worried.
And I feel heart-broken.
And I feel an empty space and I feel brave.

Rebecca England (7)
Newick CE Primary School, Newick

Poem About Tennis

Sounds like people hitting the ball
Tastes of a drink of water
Smells like tennis, as the ball strikes
Looks as if the ball is flying
Feels like the ball is soft and ripe.

Aimee May (7)
Newick CE Primary School, Newick

Food

Crunchy apples crushed by my teeth,
Bendy bananas hanging on the palm trees.
Prickly pineapples sitting on the table,
Ready to get chopped up.

Bright red strawberries
Chewed up by my teeth.
Juicy green pears.
Chopped on the table.
Slippery and slimy melons
Dripping on the floor.

Alice Gordon (7)
Newick CE Primary School, Newick

Poem About The Nurse

A nurse is gentle to the patients
When patients are hurt
Nurse gives them some food or medicine
People are needing bandages
Lady with the lamp helped
The patients have been wounded
Blood is dripping from the dirty beds
Horrible food and drink
Flies buzzing around the room
Rats are running round the floor
People are feeling sick.
Lizards are on the ceiling.
Smelly hospital.

Kerri-Anne Clough & Rebecca Collins
Newick CE Primary School, Newick

Snow

People scuttling in the snow
Raindrops disappearing
Water icing in the snow
Grass turning white as snow falls everywhere
Cold snow dripping down on the ground
People making snowballs and snowmen.

People having fun
Being cold in the night
Everyone wrapping up in the snow
People skating and making angels
And I feel lucky having fun.

Isabella Sachs (7)
Newick CE Primary School, Newick

What You Can See

You can see at the beach,
Smelly shells,
Smelly starfish,
Smelly crabs' legs,
Bumpy starfish,
Shimmery seaweed,
Stinky crabs,
Salty sea,
Smelly wet sand,
Crunchy floor.

You can hear at the beach,
Seagulls shrieking,
Sea waves pushing,
Happy children,
Giggling like they never stop,
Children splashing up and down,
Children digging with cups.

Natalie Reynolds (7)
Rayne Primary & Nursery School, Braintree

The Sea

I can see
The cold and wavy sea
The dotted sand on the seashore
And the big waves and little waves.

I can smell
The yummy ice cream
Just around the corner
And the smelly seaweed
In the whooshing waves.

I can hear the waves
Crashing against the rocks
Boats zooming across the sea
The children swimming in the sea.

Jordan Atkinson (7)
Rayne Primary & Nursery School, Braintree

In The Jungle

Lions, tigers and panthers
Prowling through the jungle
Prowling through the jungle

Monkeys, chimps and gorillas
Swinging through the jungle
Swinging through the jungle

Bats, birds and bees
Flying through the jungle
Flying through the jungle

All these animals live in the jungle
Live in the jungle
Live in the jungle.

David Kukiewicz (10)
Rayne Primary & Nursery School, Braintree

Football

Goal!
Why?
Because I scored
Why?
Because I did
Why?
Because I have to
Why?
Because, because shut up!
Why?
Because you're annoying
Why?
Because you are
Why?
I don't know
Why?
Stop saying why
Why?
It's annoying
Why?
Shut up!
Why?
How old are you?
10.

Charlie Clipson (10)
Rayne Primary & Nursery School, Braintree

Untitled

Here lies the body of Wayne Rooney
Who scored his first goal
Which sent him quite loony.

James Howard (10)
Rayne Primary & Nursery School, Braintree

Untitled

I'm a living creature,
I live in a feature,
I live at the bottom of the sea,
And you can't see me,
I am scaly and shiny,
Sometimes big, sometimes tiny,
I have fins to make me move,
And sometimes I like to groove!
What am I?

Mathew Howard (7)
Rayne Primary & Nursery School, Braintree

Seashore

The cold, wet, wavy sea
Which swishes all the way to the shore
With all their might they push to the shore
All the sandy shells
All buried in the deep, deep sand
Some might be big or small but very pretty an all
You can smell dirty seaweed
You pick it up and smell it more
So I throw it away onto the shore.

Taylor-Rose Temperley (7)
Rayne Primary & Nursery School, Braintree

Untitled

I can see the rough sea.
I can see the big blue waves.
I can see the seagulls flying over the sea.
I can smell the seaweed, the smelly seaweed.
I can smell the soft sand.
I can hear the stones crashing on the shore.

Riley Baker (7)
Rayne Primary & Nursery School, Braintree

The Sea

Shells
That are shiny
Shells that are small
Shells that are big
Shells you can't see at all.

Yellow sand
Golden sand
Glossy sand
Wet sand
Dry sand
Soggy sand
Sand when you pick it up
You can't see at all.

The dolphin
The sharks
The starfish and the hammerhead
Sharks, they swim away as fast as they can
And you can't see them at all.

Lily Arkwright (7)
Rayne Primary & Nursery School, Braintree

Sharks' Teeth

Shiny sharks' teeth,
Waiting to be discovered in the sand,
Very old,
Very black,
Very shiny,
It looks like it's very tiny,
They are very rotten,
When you spot them, grab them,
Otherwise,
They will slither away in the sea.

Joshua Foster (7)
Rayne Primary & Nursery School, Braintree

My Pencil

You're looking a bit blunt today.
Yeah I know I ain't shaved in weeks
What are you doing tonight?
Nothing.
How about a shave?
Yeah.
Come on just get in there.
Stop, I'm going to snap.

Connor Temperley (10)
Rayne Primary & Nursery School, Braintree

On The Beach

Seagulls screaming,
The sea crashing,
And the people playing,
The fish rushing,

Fish swimming away,
Crabs crawling away,
And it's all because of
The *shark!*

Will Turner (7)
Rayne Primary & Nursery School, Braintree

Things You Can Smell On The Beach

The wet smelly sand,
The wavy sea,
The food in people's lunch boxes,
The smell shells,
The wall,
The sea,
The dry sand,
The smelly puddles.

Georgi Addington Lees (7)
Rayne Primary & Nursery School, Braintree

Argument About . . . Nothing

'What's our poem going to be about, Max?' said Jake.
Harry said, 'Let's do it about footy.'
'No I'm a bit fed up of footy, what about . . . Rugby?' said Max.
'No, footy!'
'Rugby!'
'Football!'
'Rugby!'
'No shut up,' said Jake
'Let's handle this like men.'
Jake quickly snatched Max's glasses.
'Ahh, hah, I've got your glasses
Ohhh oooh come and get them.
Come on you know you want them!'
'Ahh!' Max chucked Jake out of the window,
And accidentally turned it over.
'Cricket?' Max said,
'Cricket,' Jake said.

Max Turner, Harry Gordon & Jake Chitty (10)
Rayne Primary & Nursery School, Braintree

Walking On The Beach

You hear the crashing waves
The boats out on the sea
And loads of children climbing
Up a tall tree.

You see loads of sparkling
Carved shells lying on the beach
You feel the flowing chilly breeze
Flowing through your fingers and nose
You taste the freezing ice cream on your tongue.

Jordan Pitts (7)
Rayne Primary & Nursery School, Braintree

Young Writers - Playground Poets - The Adventure Starts Here

At The Seaside

At the seaside
I can hear the gushing sea
With stinky seaweed
At the seaside
I can smell children's smelly feet
And dried up seaweed
At the seaside
I saw a roaring splashing speedboat
And five seagulls
At the seaside
I found a crab which nearly snapped me
At the seaside
Such soggy sea weather
At the seaside
I can look for sharks' teeth, black and rotten.

Phil Carey (7)
Rayne Primary & Nursery School, Braintree

Untitled

I can see the crashing sea
I can see the shining shells
I can see the shiny stones
I can see the big blue boat moving along.

I can smell the shining shells
I can smell the salty sea
I can smell the ice cream dripping from my hand.

I can hear the crashing sea.

Brooke Stevens
Rayne Primary & Nursery School, Braintree

The Sea

I can see the bumpy rough seaweed.
I can see the shiny seashells.
I can see the round crab's head.
I can see some short sandcastles.
I can smell the salty sea.
I can smell the rough sea.
I can smell the big ice cream dripping on my hand.
I can smell the fish and chips cooking in the shop.
I can hear the seagulls squawking.
I can hear the waves washing.

Megan Larkins (6)
Rayne Primary & Nursery School, Braintree

Ice Cream

I ce-cold
C reamy
E nters your mouth

C ool
R efreshing
E verlasting goodness
A good taste
M cFlurrys; yum!

Max Turner & Scott Preece (10)
Rayne Primary & Nursery School, Braintree

Puppy

P layful puppy playing outside
U nder the apple tree
P ouncing on its owner
P laying with his brothers and sisters
Y ou must know that a puppy is the best pet in the *world!*

Nikki Caton, Amy Ramessar & Gemma Wright (10)
Rayne Primary & Nursery School, Braintree

Top Gear

T otal power
O ver-the-top challenges
P laying with super cars

G etting into gear
E verlasting madness
A ccelerating demons
R acing round the track.

George Arkwright & Fraser Ingram (10)
Rayne Primary & Nursery School, Braintree

On The Beach

The sand touches my hair,
And the birds glide in the air,
The waves keep pushing me back,
And the sharks' teeth keep shining black,
On my toe there is a crab snapping me,
And shells sounding like the sea,
The sea waves shimmer over me,
And the insects keep biting me.

James Little (7)
Rayne Primary & Nursery School, Braintree

There Was A Young Boy

There was a young boy from Rayne,
Who met Saddam Hussein,
He thought he was insane,
So he gave him a new name,
He fell over on his brain and then shouted in pain!

Jack Webb & Ben Rawlings (10)
Rayne Primary & Nursery School, Braintree

The Seaside

At the seaside I saw a little girl saving a person.
I saw a snapping crab.
I heard a roaring, dashing speedboat.
I touched the smooth, wet sand.
I could hear the children playing.

Ellan Ashton-Jones (7)
Rayne Primary & Nursery School, Braintree

I Saw . . .

I saw a spider with a tail
I saw a caterpillar having tea with a whale
I saw a man with ants in his pants
I saw a fish having a dance
I saw a buzzing bee
I saw a dolphin having her tea
I saw a turtle baking a cake
I saw a sea horse starting to wake
I saw a fly, fly up high in the sky
I saw a goose slowly about to die
I saw a cow eating a pip
I saw a sheep choking on a chip.

Megan Peters (8)
Sacred Heart Catholic Primary School, Barrow-in-Furness

My Rainbow Poem

As orange as an orange ice lolly
As red as my bouncing, bouncy ball
As pink as my Jammie Dodgers
As gold as the shiny treasure
As silver as the shiny medals
As purple as my summer dress
As I stand on the smashing rainbow.

Eden Smith (8)
Sacred Heart Catholic Primary School, Barrow-in-Furness

The Little Fly

The little fly that flew up to the sky
Said, 'Hello dear friends
How delightful it is.'

The little fly that flew up to the sky
Said, 'Hello dear pig
How delightful it is.'

The little fly that flew up to the sky
Said, 'Hello dear sheep
How delightful it is.'

The little fly that flew up to the sky
Said, 'Hello dear sheepdog
How delightful it is.'

The little fly that flew up to the sky
Said, 'Hello dear rabbit
How delightful it is.'

The little fly that flew up to the sky
Said, 'Hello dear cat
How delightful it is.'

The little fly that flew up to the sky
Said nothing
Because he was gone.

Macaulay Murray (9)
Sacred Heart Catholic Primary School, Barrow-in-Furness

Football

I like football because it's fun,
I like football because I can run,
I like football because it's got rules,
My gran likes football because she does the pools.

Football is cool!

John-Paul Byrne (8)
Sacred Heart Catholic Primary School, Barrow-in-Furness

Life Is A Rainbow

My jumper is as red as roses
My T-shirt is as yellow as the sun
My socks are as green as my snot
The sky is as blue as my earrings
My lips are as pink as my bobble
My shoes are as purple as pansies
My hair is as brown as branches
My nails are as gold as crumpets
My kitten is as black as coal

My life is a colourful rainbow!

Megan Poole (9)
Sacred Heart Catholic Primary School, Barrow-in-Furness

Up High, In The Sky

If I die and go somewhere far,
I'll write your name on every star,
For you and all the angels to see,
How much you really mean to me,
Blessed are those who give you care,
Thoughts and prayers up in the air.

Chloe Macwhannell (9)
Sacred Heart Catholic Primary School, Barrow-in-Furness

I Saw . . .

I saw a pigeon flying high,
I saw an aeroplane crashing by,
I saw rain falling down,
I saw a kite wearing a frown,
I saw a cloud flowing round,
I saw leaves falling to the ground.

Jordan Wilkinson (9)
Sacred Heart Catholic Primary School, Barrow-in-Furness

Winter Days

When the snow falls
The wind calls
If you swim in the pool
Think yourself a fool
If you're cool
Come to school
If you feel a breeze
You suddenly sneeze
After a ride
Pick up a bride
When the winter's gone
The sun comes along.

Glenn Elder (9)
Sacred Heart Catholic Primary School, Barrow-in-Furness

My Seaside Poem

Red is the colour of my bouncing beach ball.
Yellow is the colour of the glorious sun.
Pink is the colour of cracking candyfloss.
Green is the colour of the slimy seaweed.
Purple is the colour of the bouncing jellyfish.
Orange is the colour of the rippling sand.
Blue is the colour of the vast sky.
While I watch the sun go down . . .

Charlotte McDowell (9)
Sacred Heart Catholic Primary School, Barrow-in-Furness

Slowly

Slowly a caterpillar walks across a branch
Slowly a hippo walks into a ranch
Slowly an elephant walks into a cage
Slowly the tiger goes into a rage.

Tom Malkin (9)
Sacred Heart Catholic Primary School, Barrow-in-Furness

Peace/War

Peace
Peace is peach
It smells like new life opening up
It tastes like sugar, as sweet as the sun
And it sounds like friendship and people sharing
It feels like skin meeting new people
And it lives in the heart of the Earth.

War
War is as black as the night sky
It smells like burnt toast in the morning
It tastes like polish that shines the guns
It sounds like screams and anger, tearing up your heart
It feels like rough carpets
And it lives in the heart of Iraq.

Amie Atkinson (10)
Sacred Heart Catholic Primary School, Barrow-in-Furness

I Saw . . .

I looked at your poster
I'd broken your toaster
I went in your house
I bought you a mouse
I saw a little ducky
I got really mucky
I made you a dictionary
I made a friend called Larry
I smelt a bin
I touched a pin
I went to school
But the teachers weren't cool.

Kieran Hackett (9)
Sacred Heart Catholic Primary School, Barrow-in-Furness

Flowers

When I see a flower
It makes me full of joy
When I see them
If I feel sad

I feel all happy inside
It's like a feeling of love
When I see a flower.

Isabella McQuillan (8)
Sacred Heart Catholic Primary School, Barrow-in-Furness

Anger

Anger is red
It smells like smoke from burning rubber
Anger tastes like burnt chicken on a barbecue
It sounds like boiling, bubbling blood
It feels hard and rough
Anger lives in your steaming body.

David Davies (10)
Sacred Heart Catholic Primary School, Barrow-in-Furness

Monsters

Monsters, scary monsters frightening
Monsters come out at midnight

Ghouls and ghosts come out the most

They come out at night and give you a fright,
It is the great fright of monsters.

Daniel Griffin (8)
Sacred Heart Catholic Primary School, Barrow-in-Furness

Monsters

M onsters are scary
O rbs of flame surround them
N ibbling flesh
S lobbering all other people
T earing people in pieces
E ating people
R ipping people in half
S *cary!*

Liam McMillan (8)
Sacred Heart Catholic Primary School, Barrow-in-Furness

Heavenly Bells

Ding-dong, ding-dong,
Goes the bell of Heaven,
Rings of joy,
There is nothing more beautiful than Heaven
My dad is in Heaven.

Charlie Hillbeck (8)
Sacred Heart Catholic Primary School, Barrow-in-Furness

Anger

Its colour is black as coal
It smells like volcano gas
It tastes like death
It sounds like the screaming of the dead
It feels like a thousand daggers of fire hitting your heart
It lives in the heart of Hell.

Scott Foden (10)
Sacred Heart Catholic Primary School, Barrow-in-Furness

Monsters In The Night

Monsters are mean
Monsters are scary
They like to eat beans
They scare you in the night
You're in for a fright
The night's at an end now
But they'll be back
To give you more frights!

Hannah High (8)
Sacred Heart Catholic Primary School, Barrow-in-Furness

Frustration

Frustration is brown,
It smells like the open air,
It tastes like bitter oranges,
It sounds like a creaking gate,
It feels like you've lost your soul,
Frustration lives deep in the bowels of the Earth.

Curtis Rigg (10)
Sacred Heart Catholic Primary School, Barrow-in-Furness

Sadness

Sadness is orange.
It smells like lava.
It tastes like hot spicy food.
It sounds like babies crying
Sadness feels like you will explode.
It lives underground.

Ben Davies (10)
Sacred Heart Catholic Primary School, Barrow-in-Furness

Happiness/Sadness

Happiness
Happiness is blue
It smells like perfume
Happiness smells like sweet candy
It sounds like birds singing a lullaby
It feels like nice, lovely silk
Happiness lives in a child's heart.

Sadness
Sadness is black
It smells like burning coal
It tastes like sick
It sounds like a car skidding
It feels like nettles
Sadness lives on its own.

Ben Yorke (10)
Sacred Heart Catholic Primary School, Barrow-in-Furness

Happiness/Sadness

Happiness
Happiness is yellow,
It smells like freshly made toffee,
It tastes like twirled fudge,
It sounds like a candy-making machine,
It feels soft and smooth,
Happiness lives in a joyful person's heart.

Sadness
Sadness is black,
It smells like raging flames,
Sadness tastes like sizzling acid,
It sounds like gritted salt,
It feels like cursed bones,
Sadness lives in the bottom of the ocean.

Joshua Reay (10)
Sacred Heart Catholic Primary School, Barrow-in-Furness

Hate

Hate is black
It smells like fire (ashes)
It tastes like rotten cheese
It feels like you have been stabbed
Hate lives in the gloomy forest.

Kieran Miller (10)
Sacred Heart Catholic Primary School, Barrow-in-Furness

School Trips

School trips are sometimes exciting,
School trips are not a time for fighting,
'Take your coat,' your parents say
In that strange but helpful way,
When you know full well it isn't going to rain.

You can't bring your brand new coat because it's got a massive stain,
Having a packed lunch is kind of good,
You should have your sickness tablet, you know you should,
You've come home, you haven't been sick,
'Mum, Mum I need the toilet, quick.'

Abigail Earlie (11)
Shirland Primary School, Alfreton

Jack And Jill

Jack and Jill walked up the street,
To buy some cans of cola,
Jack fell down ovor Jill's feet,
And the cans were spilt all over.

The ambulance came and off Jack went,
To be patched up best he could,
A pile of cards was he sent,
He should be more careful, he should.

Lauren Minney (11)
Shirland Primary School, Alfreton

Jack And Jill And Uncle Bill

Jack and Jill and Uncle Bill
Went out for animal slaughter
They saw a deer
It thought, *I'm outta here!*
And they came running after
Then Jack and Jill and Uncle Bill
Backed into a corner
They saw just there
A big fuzzy bear!
And then the bear did slaughter
So Jack and Jill and Uncle Bill
Never again did animal slaughter
They were dead
Their bodies bled
And they were left in the corner.

Michael Ball (11)
Shirland Primary School, Alfreton

Hey Diddle Riddle

Hey diddle riddle
The lion and the fiddle
The bull crashed into the moon
The little dog snorted
Because everyone supported
The food and especially the spoon.

The cow came along
And saw King-Kong
Then little Jack Horner said,
'Hey look there, a pear!'
They both hate to share
Then Jack escaped on the moped.

Jack Marron (11)
Shirland Primary School, Alfreton

Home Time

3.25, *whoopee!* Time to go home,
I'm walking home all alone,
The bell is still ringing in my ear,
And I am still dressed in my school gear.

Chair crashing,
People bashing,
Doors opening,
Children shouting,
3.25, *whoopee!*

Cassie Judson (11)
Shirland Primary School, Alfreton

Little Bo Peep

Little Bo Peep lost her sheep,
And cried for the rest of the week,
She found a duck,
Which was no luck,
She got so stressed,
She broke her best vest,
And out popped all of the sheep.

Louise McNaught (11)
Shirland Primary School, Alfreton

Hey, Hey

Hey, hey,
Tho oat ran away,
The cow jumped over the gate,
My dog had to wait,
The goose ran away with the duck,
We never saw them again, what bad luck.

Thomas Richardson (11)
Shirland Primary School, Alfreton

Dinner Time

I hate dinner time,
We all form a line,
Everyone's pushing,
Dinner ladies are shushing.

They never fill your cup to the top,
The dinner ladies act like a cop,
The trays are too small,
And all the cups fall.

The dinner ladies ignore you,
They don't let you go to the loo,
The knives and forks don't match,
They'll tell you a joke (please get the catch).

They burn the roast potatoes,
Don't eat the tomatoes,
The broccoli is soggy,
And the steam is foggy.

I hate dinner time,
We all form a line,
Everyone's pushing,
Dinner ladies are shushing.

Jacquii Brown (11)
Shirland Primary School, Alfreton

Twinkle, Twinkle Little Car

Twinkle, twinkle little car,
Even though it travels far,
It travels all day,
Especially in May,
Because it gets,
Lots of poorly pets,
Twinkle, twinkle little star,
Twinkle, twinkle little car.

Roxann Edwards (11)
Shirland Primary School, Alfreton

Assembly

Time for another assembly,
Terrible old-fashioned songs,
They are very boring generally,
I hope the teachers don't sing along.

My poor old bum,
On the wooden floor,
Doesn't half start to feel numb,
I don't think I can take any more.

Amie Shepperson (11)
Shirland Primary School, Alfreton

PE At School

Oh no! PE today
I've forgotten my things
I think I've got to run away
And I don't know how to undo earrings.

I've got to write lines
And watch the other kids
My mum said I've got to do it five times
And I've also got to count some lids.

Nathan Hadley (10)
Shirland Primary School, Alfreton

End Of School

End of school is a massive rush,
People trying to get out of school,
Teacher shouts, *'Shush!'*
Everybody calm down,
Just be quiet for a sec,
Chairs banging, children chattering,
School becomes a sea of nattering children.

Danny Gronbach (11)
Shirland Primary School, Alfreton

Maths Lesson

Fractions, decimals, percentages and sums,
Everyone groans when maths is on the board.
The teacher seems happy enough and hums,
She acts like she's the finest lord.

She calls out, 'Get out your protractors,
We're doing angles in this lesson,
And we're also doing multiples and factors!'
Everyone, whilst moaning, does what she says.

In the middle of the class,
Everybody's bored of angles and factors.
All the pupils wish they were on the grass,
Eating their breaks and having a laugh.

When the bell finally rings,
All the children jump for joy.
They are so happy everyone sings,
That's a typical maths lesson!

Katie Walker (11)
Shirland Primary School, Alfreton

Jack And Jill With Dad Bill

Jack and Jill
And their dad Bill
Went up a mountain
To see the pretty fountain.

Jack ate a sweet
And saw his mate Pete
Their dad had packed a snack
In a blue and green backpack.

When they got to the top
There was a big pop
It was his mate Pete with a balloon pump
And it made Jack shake and jump.

Craig Ashmore (11)
Shirland Primary School, Alfreton

Little Bo Peep

Little Bo Peep lost her sheep,
And couldn't be bothered to find them,
She went to the mall,
And had a great ball,
When she got home,
She found them playing her trombone,
She went so red,
And burst out and said, *'Get out!'*
And after that,
She bought a white fluffy cat.

Roseanna Foy (11)
Shirland Primary School, Alfreton

Playtime

The bell goes for playtime,
And we all rush out,
But then we realise it's the end of break,
And we missed playtime without a doubt.

The teacher takes us out but only for 5 minutes,
We don't have time to finish our game,
But it's two-nil to the other team, we shout,
Then I muttered school's so lame.

Matthew Hubbard (11)
Shirland Primary School, Alfreton

Hey Diddle Diddle

Hey diddle diddle
The cat broke the fiddle
The cow crashed into the moon
The little dog ran to see such trauma
While eating his last piece of chicken korma
And the dish ran away to Dunoon.

Leona Greaves (11)
Shirland Primary School, Alfreton

I Hate Maths

Why must we be put through
The torture of a maths lesson?
Every day at half past nine
We are forced to listen
To teachers droning on and on
About percentages and decimals
Long after the bell has gone
I hate maths.

Chunking, fractions and pie charts
Algebra and extracting data
M times five, don't forget to add H
You've not done enough, come to see me later
Problem solving, mental maths
Graphs and bar charts, don't forget line graphs
Input and output tables come last
I hate maths!

Emma Basta (11)
Shirland Primary School, Alfreton

How To Torture Your Teacher!

When you torture your teacher
You have to spell wrong and do everything else wrong as well.
You come in with no uniform on a school day
You come in and sit, relax instead of doing what the teacher says.
You always do as you please while the teacher always sneezes
Because of the sneezing powder.
All the others get more and more cowardly
They all seem to be scared.
They all seem to be trembling at their knees
You stick gum under the table but if you get caught
You tremble, you tremble.

Kieron Williams (11)
Shirland Primary School, Alfreton

Home Time

Home time at last
It doesn't come fast
Clattering of chairs
Want fresh air.

'Don't forget your letters!
Don't forget your homework!'
Shouts the teacher
As you run out the doors.

'Mum! Dad!' you scream
Running up the playground.
'Guess what I've done today
We went to a place 12 miles away
And didn't come back until
The end of the day.'

Luke Scott (11)
Shirland Primary School, Alfreton

Home Time

When the bell rings for home time
We put up our chairs
And form a long line.

Everyone dashes out the doors
And runs through the classrooms
On the carpet floors.

Everyone rushes to the bus
And shouts and screams in a rush
Everybody makes a massive fuss.

Lauren Wheatcroft (11)
Shirland Primary School, Alfreton

3.35, 3.35

3.35, 3.35
The end of the regular school day,
3.35, 3.35
The chairs go up and we race away.

We collect our books, letters and money
The loud corridors are full,
Outside it is very sunny
So the other kids continue to push and pull.

The bus has finally got here
The hall's as busy as a beehive,
We all run out and shout, 'See yer!'
Don't we all love 3.35?

Josie Jackson (11)
Shirland Primary School, Alfreton

School Dinners

School dinners, school dinners
You can't escape
Some of them have tried
But none of them has survived
If that doesn't get you
The chips will!

So if you ever have school dinners
Beware, they will get you!

Mark Mildenhall (11)
Shirland Primary School, Alfreton

Animal Poetry

Baa, baa black sheep have you anymore?
No sir, no sir only one more
If you don't, I'll stab you in the heart.

Neigh, neigh, neigh, neigh have you anymore?
No sir, no sir only one more
If you don't I'll stab you in the heart.

Oink, oink, oink, oink have you anymore?
No sir, no sir only one more
If you don't I'll stab you in the heart
OK, OK I'll only give you one.

Jennifer Worton (11)
Shirland Primary School, Alfreton

Lining Up

Fweeep goes the whistle
We all have to line up
The teacher shouts us to our lines
Someone throws down a cup

When we get into our lines
There are points for the best
Sometimes there are draws
But most are for the rest

Don't eat in the line, stand still, don't fidget
These are some boring rules
I wish I were back on holiday
In those lovely swimming pools.

Connor Hutchinson (11)
Shirland Primary School, Alfreton

We're Late, We're Late!

'Mum, Mum we're late!'
'You'll miss the bus at this rate.'

'Mum, Mum where's my top?'
'I don't know but the bus will soon be at the stop.'

'Mum, Mum the bus has gone!'
'He'll take you, good old John.'

'John, John we've got no fuel,
I'm really, really late for school.'

'Mrs, Mrs, sorry I'm late,
The car stopped on the estate.'

Sam Pywell (11)
Shirland Primary School, Alfreton

Little Bo Peep

Little Bo Peep
In her sleep
Lost her monkeys
The dream came true
At half past two.

She went to cook
Saw one eating a duck
She went to get it
But fell in a pit
And she went home with
None behind her.

Josh Morley (11)
Shirland Primary School, Alfreton

And My Heart Soars

The blossom of the flowers,
The glow of the sun,
The sparkling of the sunrise,
    Speak to me

The crashing of the sea,
The squeaking of the dolphins,
The flipping of the fish,
    Speak to me

And my heart soars.

Lucy Bugden (9)
South Wilford CE Primary School, Nottingham

Mars

The dramatic pride,
Stampeding in the spooky graveyard,
Celebrating their evil game,
Scary people march in a strange city,
Birds flying above children's heads.

Coral Parkes (9)
South Wilford CE Primary School, Nottingham

Uranus

Dashing wind bouncing on active horses
Tiptoeing on the imaginative land
No time left in the striking bold world
Mysterious and magical
Chasing the evil winds.

Anokhi Longia (9)
South Wilford CE Primary School, Nottingham

And My Heart Soars

The gold of the forest fire,
The crackling of rocks,
The shine of the shells,
Speak to me

The motion of the seashore,
The beauty of the trees,
The waking of the water snake,
Speak to me

The cries of the jellyfish,
The roughness of the starfish,
The brightness of the lightning,
Speak to me

The freedom of the sunrise,
The movement of the spider,
The softness of the sand,
Speak to me

And my heart soars.

Connor Brindley (8)
South Wilford CE Primary School, Nottingham

Mars

War approaching!
Frightening!
While the warning is sounding!
Frosty ice.
Marching rhythms,
Vibrate loudly in my ear.
The spookiness of the graveyard,
Strange horrific rhythm,
Celebrating the approaching war.

Elizabeth Chadwick (8)
South Wilford CE Primary School, Nottingham

And My Heart Soars

The tenderness of the trees,
The birth of the sunset,
The presence of nature,
Speak to me

The rhythm of the raindrops,
The crackle of the fire,
The darkness of the night,
Speak to me

The patter of the rain,
The scent of the flowers,
The culture of the city,
They speak to me

And my heart soars.

Isaac Marriott (9)
South Wilford CE Primary School, Nottingham

And My Heart Soars

The greatness of the creatures,
The softness of the sand,
The cries of the bluebirds,
Speak to me

The sparkle of the snowflake,
The beauty of the rainbow,
The brightness of the sunrise,
Speak to me

The swiftness of the sea,
The movement of the ocean,
The mist of the mountain,
The whistling of the breeze,
Speak to me

And my heart soars.

Amy Hughes (8)
South Wilford CE Primary School, Nottingham

Uranus

Striking
Dashing through
The magical spinning horses
Strong, booming buffaloes chasing them
Lively dancing
Running and hiding
Darting and dodging
The shooting stars.

Charlie Hopps (8)
South Wilford CE Primary School, Nottingham

Neptune

Kids playing, snow fading
Ice-coated old barn
Separates the cradled tower
From the mysterious, looming house
Mist of sadness, swaying tactically
Snow clinging onto the cold peaks
Motionless midnight leaking through the closing light
Midnight coming, sun sleeping.

Elizabeth Bowley (9)
South Wilford CE Primary School, Nottingham

Angela

Her eyes are like a gleaming marble,
She has ears like the most beautiful rose,
Her lips as red as a cherry,
Her teeth are as white as a dove,
She has hair as ebony as the darkest night,
Her face as pale as a new sheet of paper,
She is as sweet as a newborn baby,
She is as beautiful as a swan.

Kirsty Barnes (9)
South Wilford CE Primary School, Nottingham

And My Heart Soars

The freedom of the rainbow,
The surface of the pebbles,
The beauty of the starfish,
    Speak to me.

The liveliness of the sea,
The rustling of the leaves,
The cries of the mountain,
    Speak to me.

The gentleness of the shells,
The beauty of the fossils,
The rattle of the snake,
    Speak to me.

And my heart soars.

Shannon Taylor (8)
South Wilford CE Primary School, Nottingham

Mrs Potter

She is as beautiful as a sparkly star.
Her hair is as golden as a bale of hay.
Her eyes are polished shiny blue.
Her lips look like a beautiful red rose.

Megan Dexter (7)
South Wilford CE Primary School, Nottingham

Animal Rhymes

A hamster has a full cheek,
And its fur is soft and sleek,
It sleeps on a cotton bed,
After it has been well fed.

Megan Elliott (7)
South Wilford CE Primary School, Nottingham

And My Heart Soars

The blooming of the flowers,
The diving of the birds,
The blossom of the summer,
Speak to me

The slither of the snake,
The gallop of the deer,
The echoes of the mountain,
Speak to me

The crackling of the lightning,
The boom of the thunder,
The glistening of the snowflake,
Speak to me

The cry of the seagull,
The spike of the thorns,
The gold of the sand,
The swaying of the trees,
Speak to me

And my heart soars.

Tom Read (7)
South Wilford CE Primary School, Nottingham

About Mollie

Her hair is as thick as a chocolate cake
She has eyes as turquoise as a curving river
Her smile is as cute as a newborn baby
She can swim as well as a goldfish
Her lips are a scarlet as a shiny red apple
She has as face like a beautiful princess
Her skin is as soft as a rabbit's ear
She has a laugh like a squeaky mouse
She is as clever as a wicked wizard.

Lauren Needham (9)
South Wilford CE Primary School, Nottingham

My Heart Soars

The tapping of the woodpecker
The beauty of the rainbow
The rustling of the spider
  Speak to me

The tentacles of the starfish
The eye of a secret cave
The shuffling of the fox
  Speak to me

The gliding of the seagull
The thumping of the volcano
The wiggling of the octopus
  Speak to me

The ripples of the water snake
The pride of the desert plains
The snapping of the lobster
  Speak to me

And my heart soars.

Katy Gamble (8)
South Wilford CE Primary School, Nottingham

Mars

In the strange deserted city,
Frightened people march, bombs drop,
Repeating rhythm,
Warning people loudly.
Terrified screams.
From hopeless people,
Children killed.

Danielle Skermer (8)
South Wilford CE Primary School, Nottingham

And My Heart Soars

The waking of the seagulls
The freedom of the snowflakes
The wailing of the dolphins
    Speak to me

The darkness of the spider
The echo of the ocean
The greatness of the rainbow
    Speak to me

The brightness of the starfish
The shine of the petal
The crackling of the leaves
    Speak to me

The rattle of the snake
The beauty of the waterfall
The rustling of the sand
    Speak to me

And my heart soars.

Mollie Price (8)
South Wilford CE Primary School, Nottingham

Lizzie

She has hair like a foreign princess.
Her eyes are like fireflies glinting in the sky.
She has a smile as big as a hippopotamus.
Her laugh is as loud as a yell for help.
She is as kind and helpful as a teacher helping you with maths.
Her voice is as sweet as a mocking bird whistling in the tall treetops.
Her cheeks are as scarlet as the sunset setting in the twilight.
She is as happy as a clown in the circus.

Esther Rowe (9)
South Wilford CE Primary School, Nottingham

And My Heart Soars

The heat of the desert,
The sound of the volcano,
The beauty of the waterfall,
    Speak to me

The tension of the snowdrop,
The calmness of the river,
The softness of the leaves,
    Speak to me

The brightness of the sunlight,
The cries of the snake,
The movement of the lobster,
    Speak to me

The rattle of the snake,
The echoes of the wind,
The gentleness of the jellyfish,
    Speak to me

And my heart soars.

Macauley Robinson-Fisher (8)
South Wilford CE Primary School, Nottingham

Sunken Cathedral

Monks singing beautifully over the deadly sky-blue sea.
Ghostly ancient ruins quivering fiendishly over the deep blue sea.
The humongous clock tower, towers greatly before the deep dark sea.
The chimes of the old cathedral bells sounding over you.
The giant cathedral standing grandly before you.
Ripples in the ghastly cathedral withering slowly away.

Georgina Bird (9)
South Wilford CE Primary School, Nottingham

And My Heart Soars

The shine of the crystal
The playing of the children
The sound of the music
Speak to me

The softness of the sand
The brightness of the sun
The sparkle of the pebbles
Speak to me

The squawk of the parrots
The rattle of the snakes
The noise of the monkeys
Speak to me

The heartbreak of the person
The hug of the family
The smile of the face
Speak to me

And my heart soars.

Shannon Pendergast (8)
South Wilford CE Primary School, Nottingham

Simile Poem

She is as lively as a cheerful kitten,
She is as short as an elephant's leg.
Her eyes are as turquoise as the deep blue sea,
Her smile is as great as a queen's,
Her hair is as curly as the crashing waves.
Guess who?
It's Katy Gamble.

Lianna Hastie (9)
South Wilford CE Primary School, Nottingham

And My Heart Soars

The rise of the dolphins
The freedom of the snowflakes
The flowing of the waterfall
Speak to me

The blazing of the sunset
The echoes of the sea
The birth of the rainbow
Speak to me

The tranquillity of the seashore
The shimmers of the pebbles
The swiftness of the seagull
Speak to me

The gentleness of the spider
The liveliness of the lobster
The angles of the crystal
Speak to me

And my heart soars.

Abbie Edmonds (8)
South Wilford CE Primary School, Nottingham

Happiness Is Like!

Playing on a big bouncy castle.
Riding on my red and black bike.
Climbing on the long apparatus.
Footballing with Mac.
Having lunch with my friends.
When it is home time.

Thomas Hazledine (8)
South Wilford CE Primary School, Nottingham

And My Heart Soars

The beauty of the rainbow,
The gentleness of the waterfall,
The noise of the river,
> *Speak to me.*

The brightness of the sunset,
The waking of the sunrise,
The greatness of the sand,
> *Speak to me.*

The rattle of the water snake,
The motion of the breeze,
The freedom of the fish,
> *Speak to me.*

And my heart soars.

Rhia Brindley (8)
South Wilford CE Primary School, Nottingham

Toad

There once was a toad with a belly
So big it looked like jelly
His thirst was so bad
The animals got mad
He should have been put on the telly.

Shauna Mullins (8)
South Wilford CE Primary School, Nottingham

Happiness Is Like . . .

Going to the park and playing on the shiny climbing frame.
Swimming in the warm pool with the sun shining on it.
Going to my dad's on a beautiful sunny day at the weekend.
Going to the airport on a lovely Sunday morning.
Riding my bike to West Park near me.

Ellie Irvine (8)
South Wilford CE Primary School, Nottingham

And My Heart Soars

The greatness of mirages,
The echoes of the forest fires,
The freedom of the creatures,
    Speak to me.

The pride of the starfishes,
The uniqueness of the fossils,
The beauty of the sunrise,
    Speak to me.

The motion of the volcanoes,
The gentleness of the spiders,
The wilderness of the lobsters,
    Speak to me.

The softness of the desert,
The booming of the thunder,
The gentleness of the ice crystals,
    Speak to me.

And my heart soars.

Nicholas Belfitt (9)
South Wilford CE Primary School, Nottingham

Mr Skirton

His hair is as spiky and as cool as a hedgehog's back,
His eyes are as blue as the ocean,
His smile is as bright as the sun,
He can dance as well as Justin Timberlake,
He has a laugh like a sepia horse,
He has a voice like a platinum angel,
He can play basketball as well as Michael Jordan,
He looks like a bronze pharaoh.
    And his name is Mr Skirton.

George Alexander (9)
South Wilford CE Primary School, Nottingham

The Man

His hair is as brown as mud
And as spiky as a bunch of thorns
He has eyes like dark chocolate
His voice is like a terrified monkey
He runs like a galloping horse
His skin is as soft as warm sand in the sunshine.

George Twiddy (8)
South Wilford CE Primary School, Nottingham

Harvey

H arvey likes Mrs Coles
A nimals are lovely
R ainbows look nice
V egetables are good for me
E ight days until I'm going on my holiday
Y ellow custard is my favourite.

Harvey Fielden (6)
Turvey Lower Foundation School, Turvey

Robbie

R obbie likes water.
O ranges are yummy.
B rilliant at work.
B est at football.
I nstruments are nice.
E ats his food.

Robbie Williams (6)
Turvey Lower Foundation School, Turvey

Hayden

H ayden has put his hand up
A hit aimed at Hayden
Y awning Hayden
D angerous Hayden
E ddy is Hayden's second name
N eed more fingers.

Hayden Abeynaike (6)
Turvey Lower Foundation School, Turvey

Sammy

S amantha is sensible,
A ccidentally I ate an avocado,
M aria is my friend,
M rs Coles is my teacher,
Y ellow is a nice colour.

Samantha Caine (6)
Turvey Lower Foundation School, Turvey

Annie

A nnie is an angel.
N elly is my friend.
N aughty Annie knocked Nelly.
I like Paige.
E llie is lovely.

Annie Wallace (6)
Turvey Lower Foundation School, Turvey

Grace

G rapes are her favourite fruit.
R ather than milk she prefers dark chocolate.
A ged six.
C artoons are her favourite TV.
E xtraordinary girl.

Grace Venables (6)
Turvey Lower Foundation School, Turvey

Acrostic Poem

H aza is my nickname,
A nd I play football every day,
R onaldinho is the best footballer in the world,
R onaldo is too!
Y ou will see me play with them one day.

P erhaps if I train hard I might,
R eally play in the premier league,
I t is my dream to play football,
C helsea academy and one day,
E ngland!

Harry Price (9)
Wendover CE Junior School, Aylesbury

Where Teachers Keep Their Pets

Miss Mog has got a frog,
That hides in her bag.
Mr Mat has a rat,
That lives in his fluffy mat.
Mrs Punkey has a monkey,
It ate so much it's rather chunky.
Mr Log has a dog,
That he keeps in his big log.

Rhiannon Frayne (8)
Whitestone Primary School, West Cross

Shopping List

A man called Lod
Brain of a dodo
Spawn of a frog
Piece of a log
A big bad meany
Lamp of a genie
Arm of a sloth
Fur of a loincloth
Sole of a shoe
A big slimy loo
Remains of a fight
A whole camping site
A man called Lee
Memory of a tree
Leg made of bronze
A god called Honze.

Mitchell Drewson (9)
Whitestone Primary School, West Cross

Poem Charts

Mr Snail made a trail in,
Mrs Snail's pocket mail!

Mr Frog had a dog,
Killed by a *hedgehog!*

Mr Twit had a nit,
That died in a *dreadful pit!*

Mr Sport had a court,
That was full of *terrible thoughts!*

Mr Clock had a knock
And never came back *because he was in shock!*

Mr Meany was a genie
So nobody had a *cleanie!*

Ashleigh Richardson (8)
Whitestone Primary School, West Cross

Where Teachers Keep Their Pets

Mr Zig has a pig
Hiding in his unhealthy wig.
Mr Pat has a cat
Who miaows under his great big hat.
Mrs Pod has a cod
That wiggles on her fishing rod.
Miss Squirm has a worm
Who wriggles in her curly perm.

Ellie Ransome (8)
Whitestone Primary School, West Cross

Untitled

Mr Blowblow has a dodo
Bouncing in his hairy toto.
Mr My has a fly
He keeps it in his mini pie.
Mr Bit has a nit
And keeps it in his jar of spit.
Mrs Lantz has loads of ants
But nobody's ever going to see them.

Adam Davies (8)
Whitestone Primary School, West Cross

Where Teachers Keep Their Pets

Mr Luck has a duck
And keeps it in his heavy truck.
Mrs Soat has a goat
And keeps it in her sinking boat.
Mr Flue has a kangaroo
That snuggles in his smelly shoe.
Mrs Squish has a fish,
That plays about on her dirty dish.

Emily Olsen (8)
Whitestone Primary School, West Cross

Where Teachers Keep Their Pets

Mrs Flea has a bee
And keeps it with her special key.
Mr Meep has a sheep
And keeps it when he goes to sleep.
Miss Lig has a pig
She keeps it in her fuzzy wig.
Mr Hants has lots of ants
And keeps them in his smelly pants.
Mr Lare has a bear
And keeps it, now I forget, where?

Seren Noel (8)
Whitestone Primary School, West Cross

Where Teachers Keep Their Pets

Mr Cox has a fox
And keeps it in a little box.
Mr Bat has a cat
And keeps it in a bright red hat.
Dr Lonky has a donkey
Whose legs aren't straight but they are wonky.
Mr Blobby has a doggy
Who leaves it in his sister's lobby.

Anna Bevan (8)
Whitestone Primary School, West Cross

Untitled

Mr Twit had a nit and hid it in a sandpit
Mr Mug goes really far in his new sports car
Mrs Bog loves frogs and she hides them under her pile of logs
Mrs Lee ate some peas and then lost her keys
Mr Ache had a snake and hid it in a birthday cake
Mrs Ox had a fox and she kept it in a huge box.

Cameron Bateman (8)
Whitestone Primary School, West Cross

Where Teachers Keep Their Pets

Mrs Witty has a kitty,
She keeps her when she has a fitty.
Mr Frants has some ants,
He keeps them in his underpants.
Mr Spy has a fly,
He keeps it on a dickie-bow-tie.
Mr Bog has a dog,
He keeps it in his heavy log.

Peter Williams (8)
Whitestone Primary School, West Cross

Where Teachers Keep Their Pets

Mr Swine had a porcupine,
And he keeps it in his fizzy wine.
Mrs Kigs has pigs,
And they bounce in her figs.
Miss Funky has a monkey,
That was thin but now chunky.
Mr Lants has ants,
That crawled in his underpants.

Abigail Gwynn (7)
Whitestone Primary School, West Cross

Pets

Mr Glider had a spider that got eaten by a tiger,
Mr Log had a dog, which got lost in the fog,
Mr Cost had a wasp that suddenly got lost,
Mr Glee had a flea called Lee,
Mr Slat had a cat that lived in a hat,
Mr Shake had a snake that always stayed awake,
Mr Wish had a fish, which lived in a dish.

Alys Worthing (9)
Whitestone Primary School, West Cross

Animals

Miss Nab
Had a crab
Who lived in a lab

Miss Lee
Had a bee
Who ate one pea

Miss Hat
Had a rat
That was eaten by a cat

Mr Bobby
Had a doggy
Called Nobby

Miss Niger
Had a tiger
That liked to eat Fruit and Fibre.

Bianca Lakkiss (9)
Whitestone Primary School, West Cross

Vehicles

I'm going to France in a motorboat
I'm going in a truck, which can float

I'm going to London again
I'm going to Spain on a train

I'm going to Legoland in a car
I'm going in a wave of tar

I'm going to Wales in a train
I'm going with a mane.

Tom Bowen (9)
Whitestone Primary School, West Cross

Poems

Mr Pat and Mrs Pat had a cat,
That was chased by a bat and now is flat.
Mr Guy had a fly and it ate all his apple pie.
Mr Trog had a frog, which was eaten by a giant dog.
Mr Fairy had a canary that liked a glass of English sherry.

David Allchurch (9)
Whitestone Primary School, West Cross